DATE DUE

GAYLORD			PRINTED IN U.S.A.

CONQUEST OF THE SEA

Harper & Row, Publishers

CONQUEST OF THE SEA

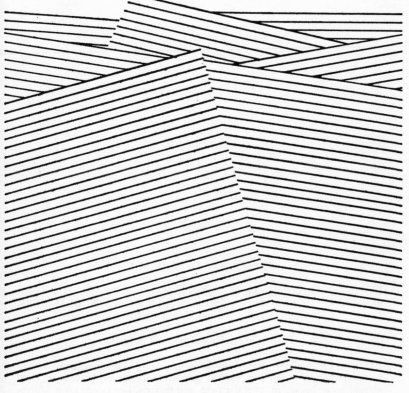

Cord-Christian Troebst

Translated from the German by Brian C. Price and Elsbeth Price

CONQUEST OF THE SEA

To Ingrid

Contents

A section of illustrations appears following page 118

Contents

CONQUEST OF THE SEA

1   Grasping for the Sea

On a June day in 1959 the lookout of an Argentinian destroyer sighted a submarine of unknown nationality off the coast of South America. It bore no identification markings, nor was it possible to recognize which fleet it belonged to from its construction alone.

At that particular period, struggles for political power were raging once again in certain capitals of South America. Liberation troops were carrying out an invasion of small Central American states, using a strange assortment of vessels, such as fishing crafts, yachts and rubber rafts. When it became obvious that the sub was trying to escape, the captain of the destroyer decided upon the severe measure of releasing depth charges. The captain's fighting spirit went unrewarded, however, for the submarine managed to get away without being identified. When on the thirtieth of June the mysterious vessel was sighted again, this time by a Brazilian naval unit, its identity could still not be determined. The first reference to it was not made until four months later.

The following October the Russian propaganda magazine *Soviet Union*, which appears in North and South America, published a report of a large Soviet submarine equipped with observation windows which had successfully completed a cruise in the southern Atlantic. It was said to be purely an exploratory vessel, a realization of the *Nautilus* of Captain

Nemo, that genial hero of the Jules Verne novel who crossed
the oceans of the world in his submarine. *Soviet Union* reported that

> armoured-glass windows were built in the sides of
> the Russian submarine. At high speeds these were
> protected from the pressures of the water by steel
> plates. If, however, the vessel reached certain inter-
> esting areas of the sea, the steel shutters would slide
> to one side, and Russian scientists could study un-
> derwater animal and plant life at their desks behind
> the windows.
>
> Now with the help of this submarine laboratory,
> ideal for long voyages at notable depths, men of sci-
> ence will be able to understand the phenomena
> of fish life and to select the most appropriate and
> efficient fishing methods. With its help, Russian
> oceanographers and ichthyologists have been en-
> abled to examine the behaviour of large schools of
> fish, discover the best methods of catching them and
> obtain a more precise knowledge of the sea and its
> mysteries.

To the general public that read about it in the newspapers,
the incident of a Russian submarine exploring the sea meant
very little. Marine scientists and strategists in the Western
world, however, particularly in the United States, were per-
turbed. The mission of the Russian research submarine proved
once again what they had been fearing all along: that the
Soviet Union is engaged in a massive and concentrated effort
to explore the oceans of the world with the ultimate goal of
ruling them—above as well as under the waves. As America's
Rear Admiral John T. Hayward, Assistant Chief of Naval
Operations for Research and Development, has often stated:
"Soviet effort in oceanography is . . . designed to establish
and demonstrate world leadership." And on the seventeenth of

February, 1960, Senator Magnuson told members of the Franklin Institute in Philadelphia: "Russia seeks to dominate the world, and to achieve this goal she must control the oceans. Her entire naval construction program since World War II has been directed to this end. Her oceanographic research program has been directed to this end."

At first glance one is inclined to think that the Russians are merely engaged in a project that other nations with a longer maritime history have long completed. Haven't the oceans been sailed and explored for centuries? Doesn't man already possess enough knowledge about the sea? Oceanographers will readily point out that this is not the case at all. Our own planet, they say, has not yet been completely conquered. It is true that mountaineers have scaled the highest peaks; geographers have explored and surveyed every continent to the far points; our geologists believe that it is hardly possible to find any more deposits of raw materials on terra firma worth mentioning; and every useful spot of the earth will soon be utilized in the production of animal and plant food. Man has sent his rockets nearly 125 million miles into space, and has hurled artificial satellites with their measuring instruments around the earth, the sun and the moon, even as far as Venus. At the same time he has only a very hazy notion of what his own planet looks like seven or even merely four miles below the surface. Here there is a mass of pioneer work still to be done. Of the 335 million cubic miles of water comprising the oceans man has only begun to know a fraction, and even in 1962 the ocean floor constitutes an almost completely unknown territory.

The well-known American geochemist, Dr. Harrison Brown, told the U.S. government, "Today, we know far less about the deep-sea floor than we know about the surface of the moon!" and according to Senator Henry M. Jackson, chairman of the North Atlantic Treaty Organization's Parliamentary, Scientific and Technical Committee, "even roughly accurate maps of the deep-sea floor exist for only about two percent of the total ocean area."

The U.S. Navy is even more modest. In a presentation before the Interstate and Foreign Commerce Committee it says that "less than one percent of the deep-sea floor has been mapped with any degree of reliability." This means that existing deep-sea maps have no, or very little, practical value. No one in his right mind would expect modern divisions to fight and win a battle—or geologists to look successfully for ore deposits—if they had to rely on ancient, inaccurate maps. But this is exactly the situation oceanographers are facing today. Existing maps of the deep sea are about as accurate as maps of the continents were in 1720.

Naturally, the question arises: how is it that this last and greatest area on our planet remains a blank? First of all, oceanography is a relatively young science. While there are perfectly accurate maps of the coastlines of the world's seas, our knowledge of the deep sea and of the relief of the ocean floor is extremely imperfect; for decades the only governmental interest shown in the oceans was exclusively for research contributing to improvement in navigation. It was the Second World War which proved how important all branches of oceanography, including marine biology, are for navigation and especially for modern submarine fleets.

Our ignorance of the deep sea is intensified by the indirect means to which oceanographers must resort in order to observe their domain. It is not so easy for them as for explorers and geologists, who have their field of activity immediately before their eyes.

Let us imagine that our planet was enveloped in a dense, impenetrable fog, and that the inhabitants of another world came to explore our earth in flying saucers. With their own eyes they could see nothing and would have to avail themselves of technical aids. Imagine them trying to measure with the use of a plumb line, and in the course of one or several orbits around the earth, the heights and depths of our planet with all its mountains, valleys, gorges and plateaus. Even if a whole flotilla of flying saucers were to carry on this task of surveying for decades, only a shadowy picture of the surface of our earth would present itself to them.

Perhaps the visitors from space might hoist on board a sample of some algae from the duck pond of a farm. As they could have no idea of the farm itself or even of the ducks on the pond, they would draw from the algae the intelligent, but for us deplorable, conclusion that there were only primitive forms of life on our planet. Or if they were to take a specimen of the air immediately above one of the steelworks of the Pittsburgh area (without being able to see the works through the cloud of smoke), what would they have but a poisonous mixture of factory gases? Our space visitors' deduction would be that animal life is impossible on our planet. Not being able to see our earth with their own eyes, they could only conclude that the earth is a heavenly body at an early stage of development, not worth inhabiting or cultivating. For ages oceanographers have been in a similar position. They possess neither X-ray eyes nor highly developed optical apparatus with which to examine larger areas of the most profound depths of the ocean.

In recent years scientists in East and West have begun to recognize the vital importance of the vast expanse of water on our planet. With mainland resources dwindling, man will soon be forced to obtain most of his food, minerals, fresh water, even energy, from the sea. But it would be irresponsible, even suicidal, to ruthlessly plunder the earth's last and largest storeroom, for its treasures are not unlimited. Responsible scientists therefore urge that the sea be cultivated rather than exploited, developed rather than harvested, and utilized in the same sensible way that has become the basis of modern scientific

farming, livestock breeding and forestry. Clearly this calls
for intensive oceanographic research on a scale undreamed of
only a few decades ago.

In the course of this research other questions vital to the
future of mankind could be answered, since the oceans have a
stronger influence on our lives than any other factor on earth.
They are, for instance, responsible for regulating the climate;
at the moment we possess too few details on how they do it.
If we succeeded in answering all the questions connected with
this subject, we should one day be able to forecast the weather
over long periods, and perhaps even control the climate for
the whole globe.

The conquest of the seas should solve a host of other problems, whose solutions have hitherto been mere guesswork. The
earth is the only planet which so far as we know has both
oceans and dry land. Why isn't it as dry as Mars? A thorough
investigation of the seas might provide an answer. Careful
examination of the sea bed will undoubtedly give a clearer explanation than we now have of the origin and evolution of our
planet and the history of life on earth.

From the military standpoint, research on the sea is perhaps
even more urgently needed than space research. In our times
national security is linked closely to a precise knowledge of
the ocean. How can we protect our coastlines from enemy
submarines if we do not know what the area in which they
operate looks like? And how will our own submarines be able
to fulfill their function in the seas of the world unless there is
exact knowledge at hand of these operational areas? America's
Vice-Admiral Momsen (Retired) had these reasons in mind
when he said: "Whoever is first to solve the problems relating
to the conquest of the sea will rule the waves. Our efforts
should be devoted intensively to the exploration of the oceans,
in order to safeguard the future of coming generations."

Yet, despite these prospects, the United States since World
War II has been lagging more and more behind other nations

interested in exploring, developing and utilizing the sea. Many scientists have blamed the American government and public for this lack of interest. In 1959 Senator Magnuson, in one of his speeches on the importance of oceanography, quoted from a letter from three eminent scientists at the University of Washington:

> The effects of this lack of interest of our government and of many of our people in the development as well as in the study of the oceans may be seen in the fact that we have now lost second place in the total production of fish to the Soviet Union and in the near future can expect to lose third place to Communist China.

(In January, 1962, the *New York Times* reported that the Peruvian fisheries' catch had become the third largest in the world, after Japan and Communist China.)

Dr. Roger R. Revelle, director of the Scripps Institution of Oceanography, gave this warning early in 1960: "At present the United States is holding its lead in the principles of oceanographic research; but it is certain that the Russians are beginning to catch up quickly. Moreover, they have been concentrating their chief efforts on extensive research expeditions throughout every ocean, and (as far as the number of research expeditions is concerned) they have probably already taken over the leadership."

The reasons for this rapid Soviet progress are not difficult to find. While Western scientists are desperately trying to convince their respective governments of the importance of stepped-up ocean exploration in order to get the necessary financial backing, their Russian colleagues have received the Kremlin's generous support for many years and are able to respond quickly and efficiently to the great challenges of ocean exploration.

At the end of World War II Russian oceanography was

almost nonexistent. As this book is written, its maritime re-search program has become the most comprehensive in the world, and its rate of expansion is considerably greater than that of the United States and possibly the entire free world combined. The number of Soviet oceanographic laboratories, for instance, is greater than anything comparable in the West. There are about eight hundred to nine hundred professional oceanographers in Russia, while several thousand young men and women are being trained in marine sciences.

Already the Russian fleet of oceanographic research and survey ships is second to none. According to 1961 hearings before the Committee on Interstate and Foreign Commerce of the U.S. Senate, it consists of more than one hundred ships, and this growing scientific armada is acquiring new vessels every year. Some of the ships are small; others, like the *Mikhail Lomonosov*, are very big indeed. Designed and built in 1957 expressly for the International Geophysical Year, it has a displacement of 5,960 tons. The *Vityaz* displaces 5,546 tons, the *Voyovkov* 3,600 tons and the *Shokal'ski* 3,600 tons. In addition, the Soviets are employing several submarines for the sole purpose of marine research. In the summer of 1959 one of these vessels, the *Severjanka*, made an undersea cruise of ten thousand nautical miles in the North Atlantic. According to *Pravda*, it has made a total of six research trips during the last two years alone. The task of the research workers on board this Snorkel-type boat was to evolve better methods of fishing and to examine the life of the shallower parts of the sea. Other Soviet submarines which are continually being sighted off the eastern coast of America are mapping the Atlantic sea bed and carrying out research on warm and cold ocean currents.

No wonder then that many American scientists and Navy officials are worried. "Today we trail the Soviets in numbers, tonnage and quality of seagoing research ships," the report of the Committee on Science and Astronautics states. "We also trail in manpower devoted to the job of exploring the seas, and probably in supporting facilities of all kinds."

Here are just some of the facts as compiled in the summer of 1961: in comparison with the large fleet of Soviet research ships, the United States had only forty-five oceanographic research ships scattered among civilian, military, fishing and geodetic activities with accommodation for only 125 scientists. (The *Mikhail Lomonosov* alone can accommodate 60 to 70 persons for research.) Most of these ships, according to American oceanographers, are old, outdated and obsolete. Two examples: In 1960 the largest American research ship was the *Spencer F. Baird*, a reconstructed seagoing tug with a displacement of 505 tons, built in 1944. And at the same time, the only American ship designed and built exclusively for research was the small, thirty-year-old, outdated *Atlantis*, whose construction was made possible by a grant from the Rockefeller Foundation (instead of federal funds) in 1931.

Perhaps the situation of the U.S. research fleet can best be illustrated by quoting Dr. Wilbert M. Chapman, director of the Resources Committee at San Diego, California. In the May, 1961, hearings before the Committee on Interstate and Foreign Commerce of the Senate, Dr. Chapman was asked by the chairman, Senator Magnuson: "You are familiar with our research fleet—"

> Dr. Chapman: Yes, sir.
>
> The Chairman: In fisheries and oceanography. Would it be a fair statement to say that it is in about the worst condition of any nation engaged in this field?
>
> Dr. Chapman: It is in worse condition than it was five years ago. . . . Let me give you an example. We stole a boat off Senator Smathers. . . . The reason for this is that the bottom fell out of our own research

ship. We just couldn't fix it up in the State of California. So the Bureau of Commercial Fisheries didn't have the money to operate two vessels in your Florida area, Senator Smathers, and were kind enough to loan one of those vessels to the State of California. We fixed it up and are using it in the State of California. That leaves you one short.

In the State of Hawaii they had three vessels working out there. One of them they put out of commission entirely, the *Manning*. The second one they didn't have money to operate, the *Smith*. She has been donated for the time being to the Scripps Institution of Oceanography because the Bureau of Commercial Fisheries didn't have the money to operate it.

We have the *Black Douglas*, an old beatup yacht from prewar days, made over, and she is being used about two-thirds of the time now because there isn't money for it. You talk about the scarcity of oceanographers. The oceanographers have to act as crew because they haven't the money to hire crews. They operate on such a basis. It is a shameful situation.

Compare these facts and statements with the size and age of the *Mikhail Lomonosov*, for example. It is little wonder that merely to catch up with the Russian lead in oceanographic vessels the United States would have to carry out a twenty-five-year replacement program within the next ten years.

In terms of manpower, also, the United States' efforts in oceanography began to lag behind those of the Soviet Union soon after World War II. According to Senator Magnuson, this country in 1959 had only 520 professional oceanographers, and for lack of teaching facilities not enough students could be trained. Some who begin their studies in oceanography do not complete their courses because oceanographic institutions cannot offer them sufficient financial support.

"Soviet Russia is winning the struggle for the oceans," Senator Magnuson told the Congress in 1959. "Scientists call it a wet war and say the outcome can determine the fate of nations and the human race. Without firing a missile, a rocket or a gun, Soviet Russia has been winning in the Atlantic, the Pacific and the Antarctic. This year she is invading the Indian Ocean. . . . Russia has been winning the wet war with more and bigger ships; more, if not better, scientists; more, and in some instances superior, equipment; and more aggressive government encouragement and action."

It was this growing concern over Russia's efforts in oceanography which resulted in three significant American studies undertaken to lay the groundwork for a systematic and coordinated long-range program in ocean exploration.

A comprehensive analysis was published in 1959 by a newly formed third Committee on Oceanography in the National Academy of Sciences, National Research Council (NASCO). It had been undertaken by NASCO at the request of several government agencies. In this analysis, the Committee on Oceanography urged an immediate expansion of America's oceanographic efforts, both for basic research and for ocean-wide surveys. In addition, attention was drawn to the military and nonmilitary potentials of the sea. Specific projects were outlined, research in the areas of new resources was recommended, and the need was stressed for the construction of new ships, not only to replace existing ones but to substantially enlarge the present American research fleet.

A parallel study has been undertaken by the Office of Naval Research. Project TENOC however, as it is called, only deals with the Navy's contract program for the next *ten* years in oceanography.

Finally, the Interagency Committee on Oceanography (ICO) has performed studies of the two above programs.

The three studies provide valuable guidance for a coordinated long-range program in oceanic research. If it were followed the United States could not only catch up with the Russians in particular fields where they have taken or shortly will take the lead, but help to bring about this country's unchallenged leadership in ocean exploration and development.

In the following chapters we will hear about the interesting proposals outlined not only by the NASCO, TENOC and ICO studies, but by scientists of other Western countries and Russia as well. We will hear about plans that have already materialized and about fantastic projects which will stir up the world in years to come.

Whether the United States will have an active part in the realization of most of these plans depends largely on Congress and its willingness to make available the necessary funds for extensive oceanic research.

How much money is needed? The cost of carrying out the recommendations as drawn up by NASCO are not at all staggering, as one might suspect. Over the ten-year period for which it was designed, the NASCO program would require $651.5 million. This is a 1958 estimate. Due to rising overall prices, the latest (1961) estimate is about one billion dollars. Still, even this sum represents only a fraction of the forty-plus billion dollars which America spends for defense annually. Another comparison: the *yearly* cost of the NASCO program would actually amount to not more than what the United States will be spending for space research every ten days in fiscal 1962.

Nevertheless, it will probably mean a hard fight if Congress is to be persuaded to grant such finances over the coming years, even though the committee which drew up the report stressed that "Action on a scale appreciably less than that recommended will jeopardize the position of oceanography in the United States relative to the position of the science in other major nations, thereby accentuating the serious military and political dangers, and placing the nation at a disadvantage in the future use of the resources of the sea."

Thus, while the United States and Russia still compete with one another to see which of them will be the first to colonize the moon, another new race has begun between them. Its goal lies not in the realm of distant heavenly bodies like Mars or Venus, but in the last and largely unexplored territory on our own planet: the depths of the oceans. In the opinion of many experts this new contest between East and West, in which Russia and the United States will be the main competitors, is just as important as the race to other worlds. Its outcome will be a matter of national survival and, as such, will influence the lives of every single one of us.

2   Conquering the Deep

On the twenty-third of January, 1960, only a few months after the studies for the three oceanographic research programs had been published, America registered a major triumph in the exploration of the deep. With a special U.S. Navy diving bell, two men were to reach the greatest known depth on our planet. On that day, crouching in a cramped ball of steel for more than four hours, they sank ever deeper into the sea.

"How much longer?" Mr. Jacques Piccard, the young Swiss scientist, asked his American companion at the instrument panel.

"Only a few more minutes," replied Lieutenant Donald Walsh, U.S.N. He had turned on the sensitive echo sounder which would indicate the distance to the sea floor. However, for the last few minutes he had been watching the instrument in vain: the graph showed nothing at all. The bathyscaphe continued its downward journey at sixty feet per minute. According to previous depth measurements taken on the surface it should already have been a long way past the ocean floor! A fit of grim humor struck the two men. "Could we have missed the bottom?" they wondered ironically. After sinking almost continuously for approximately four hours, they were now, theoretically at least, 2,400 feet below the bottom.

But then, suddenly, black marks appeared on the graph, produced by the sound waves rebounding off the ocean bottom. Lieutenant Walsh decelerated the diving speed of the bathyscaphe to six inches per second. Jacques Piccard was squatting at the tiny porthole watching the water dimly illuminated by his floodlight, as Walsh called out a string of readings: "Twenty-eight—twenty-five—twenty-four—ten fathoms!" The bottom was now only sixty feet below. The sphere kept on sinking. Thirty feet further down a grayish-white surface outside the porthole came into sight: the sea floor. Seconds later there was a very slight bump. A triumphant smile crept over the faces of the two men. Excitedly Lieutenant Walsh shouted into the underwater telephone specially developed for this dive: "Calling *Wandank!* Calling *Wandank!* This is *Trieste*. We are at the bottom. . . ."

In this instance the "bottom" meant the Challenger Deep of the Marianas Trench on the floor of the Pacific, "the deepest known hole in the deepest ocean." It is 35,800 feet below sea level. A mountain as high as Everest could disappear in this abyss; and even if a structure six times as high as the Eiffel Tower were added to it, the tip would still remain hidden some 868 feet beneath the waves of the Pacific.

For twenty minutes the two divers stared through the eight-inch-thick Plexiglas window of their sphere to observe a world which until then had been unviewed by man. They watched the clouds of silt churned up by their vessel, which had lain almost undisturbed on the sea floor for millennia, slowly settle again. It was then that they spotted a fish. Imagine a sign of life at this tremendous depth! About a foot long, it had its eyes on the sides of its head—just like a sole. They also saw a "beautiful red shrimp" measuring about an inch. For the first time a beam of light struck these creatures which were able to survive in eternal darkness under such tremendous pressure. After the dive Jacques Piccard recalled: "Here, in an instant, was the answer that biologists had asked for decades. Could life exist in the greatest depths of the ocean? It could!"

Lieutenant Walsh added: "To have seen not just one but two live creatures at the bottom, especially with the equipment we had, was staggeringly lucky. It was the equivalent of seeing a rare animal while sealed in a small steel ball on top of Mount Everest for twenty minutes in the middle of the night with no means of illumination but a flashlight fixed to the side of the sphere."

After twenty minutes it was time for the ascent from the underworld. Three hours and seventeen minutes later the conning tower of the *Trieste* surfaced again 250 miles southwest of Guam. The destroyer escort *Lewis* and the auxiliary ship *Wandank* stood ready to receive the two members of its crew. As they climbed out of their sphere, their limbs stiff and blue with cold, Lieutenant Walsh threw overboard a flat, weighted plastic container with the American flag in it. Slowly it sank to the bottom of the Marianas Trench.

In the world's leading newspapers only one or two columns were devoted to Project Nekton (so called after sea life which, in contrast to plankton—drifting plant and animal life—can swim against the current), for Walsh's and Piccard's achievement was soon overshadowed by other news. Just as the first rockets were not granted the importance which they enjoy today, so it will be some time before the general public grasps the significance of the *Trieste*'s successful dive. The descent to the floor of the Marianas Trench marks not only a new diving record, but a successful advance into a completely new world. It means the entering of unknown territory on our planet, the penetration of a region which had appeared quite inaccessible only a few years ago.

With the *Trieste*'s dive in the Pacific, forty-seven times as deep as any submarine could go at that time, the conquest of the sea reached a decisive stage. The *Trieste* began the exploration of deep "inner space" in the same way that the first earth satellites were the early steps in the conquest of "outer space."

While astronauts are seeking to fly further and further into the universe, hydronauts are striving to penetrate deeper and deeper into our own planet.

Reaching the ocean bottom in suitable submersibles is just as adventurously exciting and significant as flight to the heavenly bodies. The actual beginning of this venture came years ago with a lean American scholar and his (by modern standards) primitive deep-sea bell: the zoologist William Beebe and his bathysphere. Beebe descended only about a half-mile beneath sea level. Although that was a record in his day, it was only a fraction of the depth that Walsh and Piccard attained in 1960. One immediately wonders: why did it take as long as thirty years to develop a vessel with the capabilities of the *Trieste?*

The answer lies in the peculiar nature of the domain which Russia and the United States are just beginning to explore. Even today it is far more difficult to descend four miles, or for that matter only one mile, into the sea than to attain a similar height in the air. The pressure of the water increases the further one descends. Without protection a man would swiftly be crushed to a pulp. Modern nuclear submarines which can just about operate at nine hundred feet below sea level would disintegrate at three thousand feet like empty matchboxes under a sledge hammer. At these depths the pressure is measured in tons, not pounds per square inch.

After his successful dive Lieutenant Walsh reported that at about 32,400 feet a strong, muffled explosion caused the *Trieste* to shake as if it were going through a slight earthquake. It turned out that one of the observation windows had cracked. Walsh and Piccard felt the shock in every limb, and no wonder, for the surface of the *Trieste* sphere was at this depth resisting pressures in excess of one hundred thousand tons—in other words, the equivalent of the weight of two giant aircraft carriers.

Fortunately the crack in the pane was not dangerous, since it was on the outside of the entrance shaft and not in the wall of the sphere itself.

It was mainly because of the dangerous pressure conditions that airplanes had already attained a height of 47,472 feet, and a stratospheric balloon 71,177 feet, when Beebe and his colleague Otis Barton broke the existing depth record in the bathysphere in 1930. "Six hundred feet down—only dead men have sunk below this!" Beebe called out in his excitement as the bathysphere continued its journey into the unknown.

It has since been discovered that Beebe's and Barton's attempt was almost suicidal. The bathysphere was a ball of chilled cast iron. In 1950 tests using up-to-date instruments on the ball (it is now in the New York Aquarium) indicated that its wall contained several internal cavities which seriously impaired its strength. But Beebe and Barton did not know that when they let themselves down from the side of their research ship by means of a long, firm steel cable. Except for a thin telephone wire this cable was the only connection the men had with the outside world during the experiment.

In 1930 Beebe and Barton reached a record depth of 1,400 feet. After surfacing, the American explorers described a world of wonders such as no living soul had ever imagined existed on our planet. And during another dive Beebe felt that "here I was privileged to peer out and actually see the creatures which had evolved in the blackness of a blue midnight which, since the ocean was born, had known no following day; here I was privileged to sit and try to crystallize what I observed through inadequate eyes and interpret with a mind wholly unequal to the task. To the ever-recurring question, 'How did it feel?', . . . , I can only quote the words of Herbert Spencer, I felt like 'an infinitesimal atom floating in illimitable space.'"

Nowadays we are more prosaic. Beebe's excitement, his bewilderment and enthusiasm are only conceivable when one

realizes that he was the first person to peer into a hitherto un-
seen world. But his words, "Until we have discovered the way
to another planet, the sea bed is the most wonderful and fascinating place imaginable," are equally as applicable today as
they were then.

In 1934, after further attempts, Beebe finally reached a
depth of just over 3,028 feet. Then came the outbreak of the
Second World War. Fifteen valuable years were to pass before the first attempt was made to beat Beebe's record. It was
Beebe's colleague, Otis Barton, who in 1949 intended to
descend to a depth of 3,300 feet in his benthoscope not far
from the island of Santa Cruz. However, his floodlight broke
down after two-thirds of the planned depth had been reached
and he had to give up.

Barton's benthoscope was a steel sphere; the bathysphere,
which Barton had developed himself, served as a model in its
construction. It was also lowered by means of a long cable.
But although Barton eventually reached a depth of 4,050 feet
with it, the great disadvantages of his simple diving principle
were clear to him. His bell not only swung backward and
forward like a huge pendulum on the end of the steel cable,
but used to rotate around its own axis as well, which made it
extremely difficult to observe the marine life outside its small
portholes. Above all, its maneuverability was extremely limited.
It could only be lowered or raised by means of a motor winch
on board a barge. Therefore the deep-sea explorer was not only
limited to a very small observation area, but also faced the risk
of being caught on underwater crags. Beebe describes an occasion on which he almost crashed against a ledge of rock. In
order to move the bell horizontally a barge had to tow
it away in the direction indicated by the explorer inside. In the
process of doing this not only did the bell begin to swing, but
there was also the danger that the cable might get caught on an
obstacle which the explorer could not see.

As the depth increased, so did the weight of the steel cable holding the bell. An enormously strong winch would have been necessary in order to lower it any deeper into the sea. Moreover, because of the limited supplies of oxygen which Beebe and Barton could take with them, each dive could rarely last more than two hours.

Under these circumstances, it was possible to get a glimpse of deep-sea life, but not to make any detailed study of it. The next logical step was to develop more mobile, self-propelled submersibles—in other words, actual deep-sea vessels. This meant the end of diving attempts in bulky steel spheres.

No name is as prominent in the development of modern deep-sea diving apparatus as that of the Swiss physicist Auguste Piccard. Shortly after Beebe's dives he reached the conclusion that greater depths could be attained only in vessels that were quite independent of the surface. They shouldn't stand in a "dog and chain" relationship with the mother ship, but should be in a position to travel in any direction at will. What was most important, however, was that after diving they should be able to surface again on their own power. The problem was to give them the necessary floatage so that they would not sink to the bottom like rocks.

Toward the end of 1948 so much progress had been made on the bathyscaphe that he decided on his first trial. The first attempt, during which the FNRS-2—as Piccard named his diving craft—was maneuvered by remote control from the mother ship, improved on Barton's record and it reached a depth of 4,600 feet. Then, on its own power, it rose to the surface again.

The FNRS-2 was extraordinarily ingenious in construction. Piccard, like Beebe, made use of a steel sphere to accommodate the crew. But instead of suspending it from a steel cable he attached it to a large float filled with gasoline. This float, divided into several compartments, was to all intents and purposes a balloon. Its gasoline content (which is lighter than sea water) provided the necessary lifting power. A certain amount of gasoline, the Swiss scholar had calculated, would be just sufficient to keep the heavy steel sphere with its crew of two plus a certain quantity of ballast on the surface.

The FNRS-2 can start its diving maneuvers as soon as the hatch of the passenger chamber has been bolted. Two compartments at either end of the float are flooded; the FNRS-2 loses its "equilibrium" and because of its increasing weight begins to submerge until it finally disappears beneath the waves.

In the bottom of the float are two openings where the magnetically attached iron-shot ballast is released. These openings also allow the sea water to enter the float, compressing the gasoline somewhat and ensuring that the pressure inside the float is equal to that outside. The float can therefore (in contrast to the crew compartment) be made of sheet metal only one-fifth of an inch thick. Depth has no effect upon it, since the pressure remains the same inside and outside.

If the crew wishes to descend further they simply release some gasoline (just as balloon fliers discharge their helium). As it is immediately replaced by water flowing in through the openings in the bottom of the float, the weight of the FNRS-2 increases and its submersion rate can rise as high as sixty feet per minute. Professor Piccard reported that he was frequently compelled to release ballast to decelerate his descent, but that upon surfacing he often found part of the ballast on the FNRS-2's deck. He had thus overtaken the discharged ballast!

Piccard also avoided the danger of the FNRS-2 landing too forcefully by inventing the so-called guide chain. The end of this chain, suspended beneath the hull of the vessel, is the first thing to touch the bottom. As it gradually comes to rest on the ocean floor the FNRS-2 loses the weight of the chain. The guide chain thus has the same effect as ballast. It slows up the diving vessel's rate of fall, until it finally settles smoothly on the bottom.

When the crew want to ascend again, they need only release the rest of the ballast and, if necessary, the guide chain. This decreases the weight of the FNRS-2, which becomes lighter than the water it displaces and starts rising to the surface. Very often this happens so rapidly that they even have to brake the ascent. The explorers cannot gather up the jettisoned ballast, but they can release more gasoline instead.

After the first successful trial dive by the unmanned FNRS-2, Piccard was very confident. He eagerly looked forward to descending into the realm of eternal night himself, but a storm in which the FNRS-2 was damaged temporarily ruined the professor's hopes. Nevertheless, even the unmanned trial descent caused something of a sensation. Almost simultaneously two nations suddenly seemed to realize that it was, after all, important to be able to reach great depths in the sea. Surprisingly enough, these two nations were not the United States and the Soviet Union, but Italy and France. It is very likely that in the first instance military reasons prompted the Italian government to make a generous offer: Piccard was invited to develop a second deep-sea diving vessel for the Italians according to his own new plans. That is how the famous *Trieste* came into existence, in 1953.

Meanwhile under an agreement with Piccard the French Navy had the FNRS-2 repaired, for two of their officers, Lieutenant George S. Houot and First Engineer Pierre Willm, to carry out deep-sea dives for France. The diving vessel was renamed the FNRS-3.

Thus there began as early as 1953 a small-scale contest between France and Italy, as a series of trial dives took place on both sides. Greater and greater depths were reached. On the twelfth of August, 1953, Houot and Willm attained a depth of 4,920 feet with the FNRS-3. Two days later they got as far as 6,890 feet deep.

In the meantime Professor Piccard, with Swiss and Italian support, had not been idle with trials on the *Trieste*. On the thirtieth of September he and his son Jacques touched the bottom of the 10,300-foot-deep Gulf of Naples, which meant that they had "sunk lower" than man had ever done before on sea or land, for the bottom of the deepest land shaft in the world, the Champion Reef gold mine in India, lies at a depth of "only" 9,653 feet.

Piccard had proved that it was possible not only to reach the greatest depths with a special vessel, but also to rise again to the surface using the vessel's own power, instead of being dependent on a winch and cable. Now it was a question of profiting from the experiences of the first dives, making alterations on the boats and, if possible, plunging to even greater depths. The first success fell to the two French naval officers on the fifteenth of February, 1954, when they dived off Dakar with their FNRS-3, to a depth of 13,287 feet.

Two and a half miles below sea level! On a highway we could walk this distance in an hour without any trouble and with very little danger. But at that depth a crack of a hair's breadth in the walls of the gondola is all that would be necessary for the influx of water to slash the crew with the sharpness of a razor. The very fact that the *Trieste* and the FNRS-3 withstood this pressure was an enormous success for modern diving techniques.

It was after this record dive that the U.S. Navy developed a sudden interest in the peculiar vessel and during the summer of 1957 vigorously supported a series of twenty-six dives by the *Trieste* in the Mediterranean. The Italians took full advantage of this opportunity. While the French were attempting new diving records with the FNRS-3, Italy sold the *Trieste* to the U.S. Office of Naval Research for the sum of $200,000. In August, 1958, the diving vessel was brought to the port of San Diego, California, and delivered to the U.S. Navy Electronics Laboratory.

A modification of the *Trieste* had become imperative. To make deeper dives it must be able to hold more ballast and more gasoline. The most necessary improvement, however, was a new crew compartment with thicker walls. Professor Piccard had already planned the first steps. In January, 1959, he ordered a new sphere from the famous Krupp Werke in Germany.

They built the gondola out of three, not two steel sections. The inside diameter was 6 feet 4.5 inches and the thickness of the walls 5 inches. As two windows had to be built in, in addition to the hatch, these spots produced a considerable weakening in the wall of the sphere. So it was made correspondingly thicker in two places. The windows and the door were then bored conically into these two bulges. The outside diameter of the windows was 16 inches, whereas the inside diameter was merely 2½ inches. The field of vision was thus quite extensive in spite of the small inside diameter. Suitably shaped Plexiglas cones were fitted for windows. The entrance hatch to the bell might well be compared with the door of a safe. It was manufactured with the greatest precision to shut as tightly as possible. Since its inside (16 inches) was smaller than its outside diameter great water pressure squeezed it firmly into the hull. Eventually in the early months of 1959 the three parts were glued together with a new industrial adhesive.

All the *Trieste*'s instruments had to operate from within. The electric cables, enclosed in watertight sockets, came from inside. For this purpose twelve holes were drilled in the bulge around one of the windows. On the outside these holes measured only 8/100 inch but they doubled their size on the inside. Why the different width if the cable was to be only 8/100 inch thick? Supposing the cable should disintegrate; the sea water would then force its way into the bell. If the inside diameter were the same as the outside the jet of water entering at any great depth would have the same effect as machine-gun fire. But by doubling the hole's inside diameter, the primary force of the jet was reduced to such an extent that the water would trickle in harmlessly as if from a tap, and be insufficient to fill the gondola too quickly.

Barely five months after work was started on the bell it was built and ready for use, a white-enameled monster weighing thirteen metric tons. It was packed in a large wooden crate and shipped to San Diego, where it was attached to the *Trieste*'s float, which had meanwhile also been modified. The latter now measured 50 feet in length and was 11 feet 6 inches wide. It held 33,000 gallons of gasoline, which would give the vessel an upward lift of 125 tons.

A tube 25 inches in diameter serves as an entrance tunnel leading from the top of the float to the antechamber of the gondola below. During a dive this tube is filled with water, so that it could be made of thin sheet metal, like the float.

On the fifteenth of November, 1959, the modified *Trieste* attained a depth of 18,150 feet, a mile more than Houot and Willm had achieved five years earlier. The two crew members on this dive were American zoologist Dr. Andreas B. Rechnitzer (director of Project Nekton) and Jacques Piccard.

After surfacing they reported that "a thousand feet below sea level the water darkened to midnight black, but at 1,500 feet the phenomenon of bioluminescence gave the illusion of a starry night. Numerous tiny greenish white lights surrounded us. At 6,000 feet the quantity of living underwater lights dwindled and once again it was black."

"It won't be very long now," was the prophetic comment of the son of the *Trieste*'s designer, "before we will reach the floor of the Marianas Trench, the greatest depth on earth known to man."

It was indeed Jacques Piccard who made this prophecy come true. As described earlier, the *Trieste* successfully achieved a depth of 35,800 feet. (Later computations and recalibration of the *Trieste*'s depth gauges showed that there had been an error of 2,000 feet in the depth of 37,800 feet announced originally. Ironically it was this error that caused the Russians to announce hastily that they were building a diving ship to go 37,800 feet.)

The era of the conquest of the deep had now begun in earnest. The table below shows the impressive stages which were of most importance in the descent to the deepest known "abyss" on our planet:

Greatest depths reached by man

Atomic submarines	estimated	900 ft.
Beebe/Barton	1930	1,400 ft.
Beebe/Barton	1934	3,028 ft.
Barton	1949	4,500 ft.
Houot/Willm	1953	4,920 ft.
Houot/Willm	1953	6,890 ft.
Piccard, Sr./Piccard, Jr.	1953	10,300 ft.
Houot/Willm	1954	13,287 ft.
Rechnitzer/Piccard, Jr.	1959	18,150 ft.
Walsh/Piccard, Jr.	1960	23,000 ft.
Walsh/Piccard, Jr.	1960	35,800 ft.

In less than three months the depth attained by the *Trieste* had been doubled. A much greater part of the ocean was now accessible to U.S. explorers than only a few years before.

Shortly after the record-breaking dive by Piccard's vessel Dr. Andreas B. Rechnitzer said, in a stirring speech before the House Committee on Science and Astronautics, "Carrying two men seven miles below the ocean's surface this scientific break-through has opened all the ocean waters to exploration and exploitation."

Rechnitzer's assertion is no exaggeration when considered in the light of the following figures: Even the most up-to-date submarine cannot reach more than 5 percent of the complete ocean floor on account of its limited diving capacity. On the

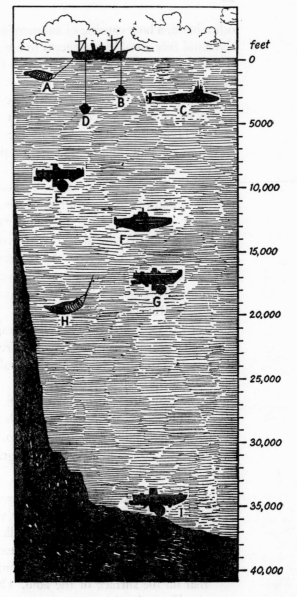

Some record depths: A. 1,700 feet: fishing nets; B. 3,028 feet: Beebe and Barton, 1934; C. 3,300 feet: future atomic submarines; D. 4,500 feet: Barton, 1949; E. 10,300 feet: A. and J. Piccard, 1953; F. 13,287 feet: FNRS-2, 1954; G. 18,150 feet: J. Piccard and Rechnitzer, 1959; H. 20,000 feet: deep-sea nets, Valdivia Expedition, 1898–99; I. 35,800 feet: J. Piccard and D. Walsh, 1960.

other hand, a boat capable of submerging to a depth of twelve thousand feet would have access to any point on one-third of the total sea bed in its operations. That is a considerable achievement. Yet if the depth it can attain is increased to eighteen thousand feet, the crew has access to any given point on no less than 90 percent of the sea floor. Should the boat possess diving capacity similar to the *Trieste*, it could submerge to the remaining 10 percent of the deep-sea floor.

The practical applications of this fact are enormous: submersibles like the *Trieste* can operate in all depths of the world's oceans. With certain limitations, to be considered later, the crew can inspect the sea floor anywhere, and amass an abundance of scientific data, which could only be obtained with difficulty, if at all, from the surface.

"No net, no sounding device, not even sonar gear can truly replace a diving boat!" declared the American oceanographer, Dr. Roger Revelle.

The *Trieste* demonstrated this clearly enough. It ascertained that the floor of the Marianas Trench was not as deep as indicated by previous measurements taken by echo-sounding from the surface.

Most oceanographers share the opinion that deep-sea research vehicles, similar to or better than the *Trieste*, will be needed in the coming years. In its report, *Oceanography 1960 to 1970*, the Committee on Oceanography of the National Academy of Sciences states:

> For a wide variety of exploratory and experimental problems the investigator would like ideally to go down to the sea-floor, walk around, observe, and collect specimens, and see to what extent the environment on or near the bottom of the sea is like that on the surface of the land. The scientist would also like to be able to use as many of his land-learned

techniques as possible. Existing bathyscaphes provide a first approach to this ideal and greatly improved submersibles are needed to complement the limited research capabilities of surface ships.

Clearly, direct observation of the sea floor permits oceanographers to select the samples they are actually looking for; they no longer need depend on chance, as they have to if probing the sea from the surface.

Indeed, the *Trieste* is already using some important instruments for investigating great depths at firsthand. These scientific and technical tools, which have been procured or built by the Navy for operation of the craft or for scientific measurements, include: motion picture and still cameras; high-intensity lights sufficiently protected to work under extreme pressure; devices for indication of depth from the surface to the lowest parts of the ocean floor; telephones for communications between the bathyscaphe and surface ships; devices for underwater temperature measurement; water samplers; photometers for measuring water transparency and sedimentation; tape, graphic and other data recorders; specialized equipment to measure radioactivity in the water and sediments; meters for measuring the craft's velocity of descent, ascent and horizontal motion in the water; and a number of specialized acoustic devices.

In addition, a plankton collector developed by Dr. Rechnitzer has been mounted on the *Trieste*'s deck. It consists of a set of nets that can be made to sample and store captured plankton when actuated from inside the sphere. Each one will then contain a sample of life from a given depth. A thermometer automatically records the temperature at each depth.

A similar process has been employed on the surface for a long time, whereby special metal bottles hanging at different intervals are let down into the sea by means of a long wire.

When a weight is sent down, it strikes the first bottle and seals it with its sample enclosed. As this bottle closes, it releases a second weight which travels down to the second sampler, and so the process is repeated over and over, until every bottle contains a sample of the sea water at the depth at which it closed. In the *Trieste*'s case an electronic flash lights up the area and cameras photograph and film the immediate area around the diving boat.

In January, 1960, Lieutenant Houot said, "Investigation of the sea will in future have to rely more than ever before on deep-sea diving craft. These will constitute a true submarine laboratory, for every research worker has to penetrate into the realm which he wishes to study. This applies to the nearest heavenly bodies just as much as it does to the seas of the world."

It is obvious then that a regular fleet of deep-sea submersibles is needed to solve in the shortest possible time the numerous problems that are awaiting our scientists in the eternal night of the sea. Not only should these vessels possess the depth-reaching capacity of the *Trieste*, but they should also be faster, more mobile and more versatile for a great variety of tasks. What are the prospects for their development?

3 Vehicles for "Inner Space"

It is the tragedy of prophets and inventors alike that few people ever listen to them in their own day. The realization of vital projects, of great ideas, is very often severely delayed. Space science, a multibillion-dollar industry, would never have become what it is today without the inventiveness, enthusiasm and initiative of the small, often destitute, amateur rocket builders of the twenties. Only when the governments of individual countries—first Germany, later Russia and the United States—gradually recognized the importance of large rockets were money grants finally established. The large industrial firms also joined in the gamble on the future. A similar situation has faced, and today is still facing, many oceanographers and marine scientists.

From personal experience, the author knows of a West German naval engineer who had designed plans for a deep-sea diving boat. Naturally, as a German, he first offered to show them to the West German Defense Ministry. He received no answer to his letter. He then tried the U.S. Navy via the American Consulate. Still no answer. The British sent a polite "No." From the French Ministry of War he received a friendly reply, telling him that he would hear from them again. He never did.

In despair and in understandable eagerness to see his brain child come to life, the man finally offered to show his plans to the East German government. A reply came within a few days, asking him to be kind enough to come to East Berlin to talk over his project.

The ship designer did not go to East Berlin—either out of loyalty to the West or for some other reason. He is still trying to sell his idea to a Western government—with little luck. Of course, if ever built and tested, the boat he has designed may go to the bottom like a rock and stay there. But this is not the point. What is so disturbing is that Western governments have not even bothered to look at the plans—whereas the East responded eagerly and quickly. It is this attitude that has helped the Soviets to take the lead in the race to outer space, and it may well help them to do likewise in the exploration of the seas.

Piccard's greatest problem was the financing of his first bathyscaphe. If some government twenty-five years ago had expressed more interest in the plans of a professor who was "mad" about the deep sea, the West would probably possess quite a number of deep-sea submersibles today. Instead, in the spring of 1962, the *Trieste* and the FNRS-3 were the only deep-sea diving boats in the service of the Western world. Moreover, despite the depths attainable by the two Western craft, their technical capabilities leave much to be desired.

Both vessels represent a remarkable improvement on the Barton-type diving bell fastened to a cable, but their maneuverability is still extremely limited. Although they are able to travel horizontally with the aid of a small propeller, they cannot rise or sink at will several times in succession, as might be necessary when traveling over a mountainous part of the sea floor. As soon as these vessels have shed their ballast to rise to the surface, they cannot descend again without running the risk of getting stuck in the deep. Even their horizontal radius of operation is limited by a relatively weak electrical propulsion system. In the case of the *Trieste*, it amounts to only one mile.

Dr. Rechnitzer once explained that "the bathyscaphe, as purchased by the United States, is in reality a 'Model T' of the deep submersibles. It has, however, conquered the depth barrier and points the way to more advanced vehicles. Nevertheless, as far as we know, it is still the best in the world. [But] French and Russian bathyscaphes under development will undoubtedly surpass the versatility of the *Trieste*."

The future course is clearly marked: a new, improved version of the *Trieste* "Model T" must follow.

According to American oceanographers, the spherical shell of a new submersible should have an internal diameter of eight feet, which would provide 80 percent more room than the *Trieste* or the FNRS-3. In such a gondola, it will be possible to accommodate not only two observers besides the pilot, but also permanent navigational and scientific instruments too delicate to be attached outside the vessel.

Interestingly enough, manned satellites for outer space— such as the Mercury capsule or the Apollo three-man satellite —can prove very helpful for the internal design of the new bathyscaphe gondolas. The new technique of "shrinking" various electronic and mechanical components to incredibly small dimensions has made it possible to crowd a vast array of instruments into the smallest space. A few years ago, the same instruments would have filled a small suitcase. By borrowing ideas from the missile people, marine engineers will be able to pack air generators and dehumidifiers into a diving sphere without using up too much precious space. Better heating devices will also be necessary in future bathyscaphes. On the bottom of the Marianas Trench the temperature inside the *Trieste*'s gondola dropped to 50° Fahrenheit. (After surfacing the gasoline in the float was as cold as minus 10°.) The humidity in the crew compartment was unusually high because of the transpiration of the two divers. Since there was no mechanical means of circulating the air (Beebe had been able to help himself with a palm-leaf fan), the cold air collected at the bottom of the sphere and Walsh's and Piccard's feet became especially cold. "After six thousand feet it felt as if we were in an icebox," they said in a television interview several weeks after the dive.

A more "habitable" bell, therefore, is an absolute necessity if dives lasting from six to twenty hours or more—such as are planned for future submersibles—are to be achieved. In their report, *Oceanography 1960 to 1970*, American marine scientists further recommend that a submersible should be able to maintain a top speed of four knots. This would give it a range of roughly thirty miles, or thirty times more than that of the *Trieste*. One of the chief necessities is that the submersible be maneuverable enough to surmount underwater obstacles with the aid of vertically operating propellers. For better observation of the deep it should possess at least two windows, looking both forward and down. Mechanical arms, protruding from the outside of the bell and operated from within, should make it possible for the operators to manipulate nets or instruments, adjust apparatus for use on the ocean bottom, pick up rocks or capture living creatures.

Probably no single type of bathyscaphe will be suitable for all the functions which need to be fulfilled in the course of exploring, conquering and developing the seas of the world. Therefore, various models will gradually be designed and built in ever-increasing numbers. They will serve not only as research craft, but also as "work horses" of the sea. They will supervise and carry out drilling operations for crude oil on the continental shelf, or work in ore mines at the ocean bottom. Some will have crew members, others will be unmanned; some will be based on the bathyscaphe principle and capable of deep dives, others will operate like submarines, with a few hundred tons displacement, with diesel-battery power, a test-depth of several thousand feet and a capability of staying at sea for two weeks.

Luckily, several such inner-space vehicles are already on the drawing board or have even been completed in recent months. Professor Piccard and his son completed designs for a submersible for medium depths, called a mesoscaphe, soon after the *Trieste*'s record dive. Smaller and faster than the *Trieste*, it will assist, among other duties, in further investigation of the vast mineral resources recently discovered on the ocean floor.

Just as certainly as these mineral deposits will be hauled to the surface, man will one day raise the riches lying in the hulls of sunken ships with the aid of specially designed diving vessels. The well-known diver, Harry Rieseberg, who has already raised respectable quantities of gold, maintains that invaluable treasures lie on the bottom off the coasts of Europe and North and South America, and mentions "an El Dorado off the coasts of Africa." Rieseberg strongly believes that about 80 percent of these treasures could be raised with suitable salvaging apparatus, and that they would more than cover the salvage costs.

The annual total of ships which sink is fairly high. Many of them, for instance the luxury liner *Andrea Doria* which went down in 1955, could be raised if appropriate submarine salvaging vessels were available. Should it prove impracticable to salvage the ship itself, then at least important parts of the cargo could be raised. One device that could be modified to do this is *Solaris*, a one-eyed, mechanical robot. Equipped with a remotely controlled TV camera, this spherelike tool is let down by cable from a surface ship. With the aid of two propellers it can travel horizontally and reconnoiter an area as big as a football field. If the light conditions are favorable, *Solaris* can discover objects only one inch thick (such as a submarine cable) from a distance of fifteen feet. With the aid of two strong steel claws it can grasp and haul objects weighing close to eight thousand pounds up to the surface.

Unfortunately, *Solaris*, originally built to recover missile parts fallen into coastal waters, cannot descend deeper than two thousand feet. With a manned, highly maneuverable craft of the same diving capacity as the *Trieste*, however, it should be possible to get at the *Titanic*, resting seven or eight thousand feet at the bottom of the North Atlantic, where she sank in 1912.

The German shipbuilder Henry Hartung has designed just such a submersible. Using a so-called "depth-rotor," it is speedy, maneuverable, and can hold a steel robot sphere besides a crew of two. Hartung explains: "I do not want to break any records. The purpose of my 'deep-sea helicopter' is to track sunken ships at great depths and raise their valuable cargo. It is, moreover, the most economical mechanical salvage device for airplanes, rockets and submarines that sink to the bottom."

The robot sphere, no larger than a medicine ball, is located in a shaft in the front part of the submersible. It is equipped with the most indispensable tools for manipulating sheets of strong steel, such as an acetylene torch, steel cutters and pincers. These tools, each of which is on the end of a telescopic arm protruding like a sting, are remotely controlled from inside the crew compartment. A thick cable transmits instructions to the mechanism inside the sphere. In an actual salvage operation it is lowered out of the shaft of the diving craft into a proper working position next to the wreck. Then the torch goes into action, cutting an entrance into the hull of the sunken ship. The opening can be made so large that the craft itself can follow, or further operation can be directed by remote control with the help of a built-in television camera.

Hartung's submersible looks almost like a midget submarine, with the conning tower not amidships but in the bow. The pilot stands in this tower and steers the vessel. Two quartz windows give him a wide field of vision. The observation bell is connected with this tower, the top of which also serves as the entrance hatch. The diameter of the bell is a little over six feet, just enough room for a second crew member and the most necessary instruments, including oxygen tanks.

By placing the sphere in the prow, Hartung hopes to enable his divers to bring their craft as near as possible to the object under observation. That is not possible with the *Trieste*, where the gondola hangs amidships underneath the float.

Hartung chose the name of "deep-sea helicopter" for his vessel, because it "plows" its way into the sea just as a helicopter rises into the air. Its mobility is equally great. With the aid of two horizontal propellers which are built in two chimney-like shafts open at both ends (one amidships, the other in the stern) the vessel can dive accurately to its target. It can move in any direction desired, including up or down, at will and with any desired frequency. It would clearly be superior in maneuverability to any bathyscaphe now in existence.

Thanks to these propellers Hartung's submersible needs ballast only in an emergency—for instance, if its motors fail. The continuous turning of the propellers will also "suck" the boat to the surface again. All the steering—forward, backward or sideways—is controlled by a screw mounted on a swivel in the stern. Such prominent experts as Professor Piccard and the officers Houot and Willm have inspected Hartung's plans and confirmed their feasibility. So far, no company or government has offered to finance the submersible's construction.

Fortunately, the design and construction of deep-sea submersibles today no longer depend entirely on the efforts of enterprising individuals, but are beginning to interest farsighted industrial firms. Large American rocket and aircraft companies like Lockheed Aircraft Corporation, North American Aviation and Martin Company are suddenly turning their attention to the sea. As early as 1959 both firms were considering participation in the development of submarines and diving boats.

The French Navy, together with a large engineering company, in the summer of 1961 completed its second bathyscaphe. As soon as it becomes operational, the *Archimède*, as it is called, will be able to take two men down to 35,800 feet. From within the vessel, holes can be drilled into the ocean floor to provide geological samples.

Designed for shallower depths is another so-called mesoscaphe. The plans for it have been worked out by the famous French diver Jacques-Yves Cousteau in cooperation with the French Navy. His vessel will only be able to reach a depth of fifteen thousand feet, but can remain below for four days at a time.

A more original vessel is RUM (short for Remote Underwater Manipulator), developed for the U.S. Office of Naval Research. It is the brain child of Dr. Victor Anderson of the Scripps Institution of Oceanography. Early in July, 1961, this unmanned army-type tank successfully completed shallow trial "crawls" at the bottom of the Pacific off the coast of California. Its maximum operating depth is given as ranging up to four miles. The eleven-ton vehicle is equipped with sonar gear, underwater lights, six miniature television cameras and a "master slave arm" with a fifteen-foot reach. A reel at the stern of the vehicle lets out five miles of coaxial cable to a control van parked on the shore. An operator from inside the van can steer RUM and order the mechanical arm to make five motions: wrist rotation, hand grip, shoulder rotation, shoulder pivot and elbow pivot.

The tank travels at a speed of three miles per hour and can carry a thousand pounds of instruments for research and salvage work on the bottom of the sea. "RUM will permit the intensive investigation of a selected area," Anderson explained during an interview. "For example, it could crawl down to outcroppings on the ocean floor, chip away the surface sediment, extract a sample of virgin rock, and bring it back for radiocarbon dating."

Maybe one day a whole convoy of RUM tanks will be crawling across the sea floor, searching for profitable salvage work. An improved version of RUM is already being built of aluminum, with a weight of only four tons instead of eleven tons giving it higher speed. It is also to be fitted with a rotor so that it can ascend and descend in the water like a helicopter.

In the fall of 1960 it was announced that the U.S. Naval Ordnance Test Station at China Lake in California was also working on the blueprints for a new diving vessel. It is to be more mobile and maneuverable and capable of carrying more scientific instruments. If the money for its construction should ever be granted it will be able to explore the greatest depth of the ocean floor.

Two twenty-horsepower motors in the stern will drive the vessel at a speed of 3 to 6 mph, with an operating radius of one hundred miles. The hull is designed to offer as little resistance to the water as possible. Stabilizers attached to the hull will facilitate the maneuvering of the diving vessel. A long pointed beak in the prow will carry searchlight and sonar gear.

What about Soviet deep-sea submersibles? Understandably, it is very hard to get detailed scientific information and exact data on Soviet projects. During recent years, Soviet propaganda media in West Germany have at different times reported that a "bathyscaphe far more advanced than the *Trieste*" was being built in the Soviet Union. Sometime later, Western papers reported that such a vessel had been launched in Leningrad. A report of July, 1961, however, attributed to a Soviet oceanographer and published in *Pravda*, contradicts all these speculations. In his article V. Azhazha complained that there was still no work under way to build a Soviet bathyscaphe. "To this day," the article said, "the question has not been decided of who will prepare the blueprints for and build the first Soviet bathyscaphe and who will dare to become the passenger for it." Azhazha, incidentally, also complained about Soviet backwardness in the field of underwater photography.

The *Pravda* article seems to indicate that the U.S. and the free world for the time being lead in the field of deep-sea submersibles. This, unfortunately, does not mean that government funds for their construction are readily available, even though they would not be expensive as compared with the cost of developing missiles and satellites for outer space. The price for a RUM vehicle, for example, is about $100,000, less than one-thousandth of one percent of what it will cost the U.S. to go to the moon. Because of these relatively modest costs, larger companies can therefore risk developing submersibles without governmental financial aid. One of America's leading light metal companies is already building such a vessel: the *Aluminaut*. Designed by Reynolds Aluminum and Metal, it seems destined to become the prototype of Admiral Momsen's prophesied fleet of deep-sea boats. Almost as maneuverable as a conventional submarine, it is to have a range of a hundred miles and will operate at depths up to fifteen thousand feet. Thus it will have direct access to about 60 percent of the ocean floor.

The *Aluminaut* is the first true deep-diving *boat* in the proper sense of the word. While, as we have seen, a bathyscaphe consists of a small steel sphere underneath a gasoline-filled float, the crew compartment of the *Aluminaut* is a 33-foot-long pressure hull, 7 feet in diameter, with 6-inch-thick aluminum walls. (Over-all length is 48 feet with a 10-foot beam.) Thus for the first time in a deep-sea submersible there is a chance of a relatively comfortable work room in which the observers can move about. Besides three crew members, it will hold two tons of scientific instruments.

The *Aluminaut* will have *positive* buoyancy; in other words, it will not need a gasoline float like the bathyscaphe to bring it to the surface after each dive. Instead, it will drive itself down with the aid of a horizontal propeller.

There is little wonder, then, that the U.S. Navy is keenly interested in this craft. Soon after the first successful pressure-tank tests in 1960, there were rumors that the Navy was considering equipping one such boat with an experimental nuclear

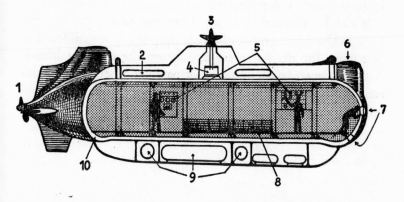

A cross-section of the *Aluminaut*. 1. Main propeller.—2. Tank for compressed air.—3. Vertical propeller.—4. Motor.—5. Instruments.—6. Entrance hatch.—7. Windows.—8. Batteries.—9. Submergence tanks, solid ballast, more instruments. Complete keel can be dropped in case of emergency.—10. Six-inch-thick pressure hull.

power plant, efficient enough to increase its range substantially.

An *Aluminaut*, using conventional electric power, will be able to stay submerged for thirty-six hours and, in case of emergency, could double this time. (The pre-snorkel submarines of World War II could not stay down any longer than this.) The *Aluminaut*, in contrast to Hartung's boat, possesses only one propeller for descending and rising in the water.

"This boat," the designers announced, "will cost less than

a conventional submarine. Moreover, it will be easy to operate." A lot of underwater work could be accomplished with
this vessel. "Magic arms," similar to those with which radioactive material is handled in nuclear laboratories, will protrude
outside the hull of the boat. Watching over closed-circuit
television, or through an appropriately thick window built in
the side of the boat, scientists will manipulate these arms from
inside the crew compartment.

It can be assumed that the *Aluminaut* represents the first
stage in the development of larger deep-sea submersibles. The
first plans for the latter are already on the drawing boards.
A fleet of such boats would be of paramount strategic significance for every naval power.

4 The Invisible Enemy

The efforts of both Russia and the United States to learn more about the sea and its mysteries are, to a considerable extent, the results of strategic considerations.

After the *Trieste* had successfully plunged to the bottom of the Marianas Trench, the U.S. Navy merely announced that the purpose of the dive was "to demonstrate that the United States now possesses the capability for manned exploration of the deepest part of the sea floor." The actual aims of the dive, however, were to find out more about the possibilities of antisubmarine warfare and deep-diving military submarines. Indeed, scientists of the U.S. Navy have been occupied with a stepped-up exploration of certain regions and phenomena of the sea connected with antisubmarine warfare since the beginning of 1959. Vice-Admiral John Smith Thach, Commander of Antisubmarine Defense Force, U.S. Pacific Fleet, Task Group Alpha, knows from bitter experience that "the ocean is a liquid jungle. Survival depends on how well we know this environment."

The seventy or so trial dives organized and carried out within the framework of Project Nekton by the U.S. Navy up to February, 1960, which reached their high point with the *Trieste* record dive, were nothing other than the first reconnaissance journeys deep into this "jungle." The knowledge gained in this way will assist at the same time in the improvement of the existing American nuclear submarines, and countermeasures against hostile submarine invaders. The Navy would like to see the depths attainable by these vessels, at present an estimated (classified) maximum of 900 feet, increased to at least 3,000 feet.

Finally, the experience gained with the *Trieste* will form the basis for the creation of a completely new kind of military submarine, capable of maximum range and depth. The deeper the boats of this type will be able to dive, and the more extensive the space in which they can hide, the less vulnerable they will be.

The Soviet Union soberly foresaw the importance of the world's deep sea as a deployment area for an invisible military fleet. Immediately after 1945, she began building submarines in great numbers. Reports to the U.S. Central Intelligence Agency (CIA) in 1959 substantiated what several American admirals—Raborn, Thach, Burke and Rickover being the most prominent—had been fearing for a long time: It is not the Soviet bomber fleet or their arsenal of intercontinental ballistic missiles which represent the greatest threat to the United States, but the powerful Red submarine fleet, with which, pessimists believe, the Russians aspire to full command of the Seven Seas —under water as well as on the surface.

Russian admirals, it is believed in both the Pentagon and in the British Foreign Office, are convinced that the Red submarine fleet would be strong enough to contend with both Britain and the U.S.A. for the control of the sea if matters came to a head. As early as 1957, Nikita Khrushchev had threatened: "Our submarines can block American ports and shoot into the American interiors, while our rockets can reach any target. America's vital centers are just as vulnerable as NATO's bases."

Raymond V. B. Blackman, editor of *Jane's Fighting Ships*, the standard reference work on the navies of the world, states that the new Russian submarines "represent a formidable threat to the Allied control of the seas, and they could wreak great havoc on . . . American and British shipping." Russia, Blackman warns, was not slow to follow the example of German Admiral Doenitz, who soundly judged that Great Britain could be brought to her knees by the destruction of her merchant shipping by submarines in the Atlantic.

In Britain, just as in America, the weakness of the national submarine defenses is criticized by some of the highest-ranking Navy officers. Admiral of the Fleet Sir George E. Creasy said in October, 1960, that Britain should participate to a greater extent in NATO submarine defenses, since it was hardly possible to counter any Soviet underwater attack with present resources. "You can be very sure that this point has not been lost to view by our only likely enemy," Admiral Creasy said.

The Soviet Union indeed possesses the largest submarine fleet that has ever existed in war or peace, and will remain unchallenged for the next few years at least. According to the 1962 edition of *Jane's Fighting Ships* this fleet was composed of 430 vessels. This is more than all other subs of the rest of the world combined and ten times as much as the German *Kriegsmarine* could muster at the start of World War II. It is significant that the Russians have their fishing craft, fruit cargo ships and whalers built abroad, chiefly in East and West German shipyards, as their own dockyards are overworked with submarine building.

At the same time, America possessed a mere 150 submarines, 22 of them nuclear powered. These, together with those of other nations of the free world, bring the grand total to no more than 302. But only a fraction of America's submarines were in service at that time. Most had been mothballed. Conning towers, nautical instruments, torpedo barrels and the sensitive electronic nerve fibers have been embalmed until the day when they might be needed. Should that day really come, it is hardly conceivable that a mothballed submarine could be made serviceable within twenty-four hours, during which time a possible atomic war might already have been decided. This is perhaps the reason why the Russians are keeping the major part of their powerful submarine fleet in continuous use, concealed beneath the ocean's protective billows.

Agency reports were not only concerned with the active building in Russian shipyards. They were also troubled by reports of various types of Soviet submarines in operation and their areas of maneuver. For instance, a pack of Soviet submarines, along with medium-range bombers, could present the greatest danger to the U.S. Mediterranean Fleet. A typical Black Sea formation would comprise snorkel submarines of the long-range W class, and smaller boats of the M class, whose primary object is to protect the coasts. Some of these have at times been partly manned by Egyptian crews in training.

One hundred and fifty Red submarines are said to be in the Baltic, and the so-called "Northern Fleet" in the Atlantic numbers a further 110, according to information released by the CIA.

Vice-Admiral John S. Thach, in an article titled "The Silent Paths of Destruction" published in late 1960 in the service magazine, stated:

> The Soviets have over 100 submarines in commission in the Pacific. In addition to these, the Chinese Communists have the 4th largest submarine force in the world. As a matter of fact, the great majority of these submarines are new constructions and their number has multiplied several-fold within the past 6 years. Units of this combined Communist submarine fleet can be supported from bases stretching from the Bering Strait, just a few miles from the new

State of Alaska, to Rainan Island in the South China
Sea. Some conventionally powered Communist submarines can operate unrefueled along the entire
coastline of North America to the Panama Canal,
the Hawaiian Islands, Indonesia and Australia, and
well into the Indian Ocean.

It is further known that the Soviet Union has turned at
least twenty-two diesel-powered boats over to Red China, and
a few others to Egypt and Indonesia. This alone would make
it obvious that the Russians are not only constantly modern-
izing their large submarine stock, but are placing great faith
in their future nuclear-powered boats.

NATO intelligence reports of January, 1962, indeed credit
the Soviet Union with eleven nuclear-powered submarines.
Next to these "Nukes" the most dangerous Soviet boats are
undoubtedly those of the Z class. Though they are only diesel-
powered, they can travel twelve thousand miles without re-
fueling, and have indeed been sighted as far from their home
bases as the North and South American coasts.

As far as was known in the spring of 1962, the Russians
had thirty missile-carrying submarines of various types
cruising the seas. Some were conversions from Z-class boats,
whose conning towers had been lengthened to accommodate
two vertical missile tubes. Another, belonging to the W class,
was photographed by an American scout plane as early as 1959
when it surfaced off Iceland. Experts considered its sixty-
foot superstructure unusually large. As the boat surfaced, the
crew hurriedly covered the stern with a tarpaulin to conceal
several barrels which were probably designed to fire ballistic
missiles.

Except for the new nuclear submarines the only other type
of Soviet submarine built from keel up for the purpose of
carrying missiles is the G-class submarine. It can pack six

Golem rockets with nuclear warheads in vertical tubes. But the boats have to surface in order to fire these missiles. On the other hand, Komet rockets, which have a shorter range, can be fired from the deck of a submerged G-class submarine. Here the Russians have apparently successfully developed a weapons system which German scientists in Swinemünde had been trying to complete for their U-boats shortly before the end of World War II.

What about the range and the firing capabilities of Russian submarine missiles? On the eighteenth of August, 1959, the very day after Admiral Burke had made the statement that Soviet submarines could bombard cities like Detroit, Cleveland or Chicago from the Hudson Bay, *Red Fleet*, the official organ of the Soviet Navy, explained: "Our boats could penetrate the Hudson Bay via the Arctic Circle and thence destroy important American targets between 750 and 900 miles away."

This assertion has an exaggerated sound to it, for the range of Golem rockets is believed to be only four hundred miles, that of Komet rockets not more than a hundred miles. But the threats of *Red Fleet* appear altogether in another light if we consider that the boats of the W and Z types, instead of carrying rockets on deck, are able to tow long-range rockets of a much improved German V-2 type in special containers right up to our coasts.

With the capture of the German rocket-test center of Peenemünde at the end of World War II, all models, plans and prototypes for the towable underwater containers for V-2 rockets fell into Russian hands. Since 1945 they have had time to develop these containers as component parts of their own submarine armory. As early as 1950 they were able to fire fifty-foot-long rockets on mainland targets from the open sea.

The idea of using towable submarine missile containers as mobile launching platforms for V-2 rockets originated early in 1944. It was known as the *Lafferenz Projekt*. These bases can, of course, only be tracked down with difficulty. Each individual container, later mass-produced in Russia in the fifties, was ninety-six feet long and, fully loaded, weighed close to seventy tons. It contained a control room, several tanks for rocket fuel as well as a gyrostabilizer by which the launching stand was to remain perfectly steady both in transit under water and during firing of the V-2.

Three such containers could be coupled together and towed by a single submarine at a speed of fifteen knots. If only one container was towed, the boat could travel five knots faster. A trip from Wilhelmshaven, Germany, to the U.S. was scheduled to take about three weeks. From Russian ports, it would take slightly longer.

Besides the gyroscopic stabilizer several rudders maintained the horizontal position of the container when traveling. They were driven by a special power unit which also supplied the current for the instruments, the stabilizer, the pumps and the control room.

In case of imminent war danger, these Soviet submarines could cruise to their ultimate destination with rocket containers in tow. Firing preparations would take only thirty minutes. The water in the front buoyancy tanks would be pumped out, allowing the containers to rise slowly to a diagonal firing position. Only their noses would protrude above the surface.

From a dinghy three technicians could enter the container through a small hatch to connect all electrical contacts with the submarine. Fuel would then be pumped into the rocket, ventilators absorbing the vapors as fresh air was drawn into the control room.

With the rockets ready for firing the technicians would return to the submarine. The boat would then submerge, and at zero hour the rocket would be fired by radio command from within the submarine. Afterward the empty container could either be towed back to the home base or sunk on the spot.

At the same time as Soviet Russia was enlarging her submarine fleet she also began to look for submarine bases abroad. Late in 1960, in a special treaty with Guinea, she obtained port facilities on the west coast of Africa. So far, she has not dared to station any of her submarines in Communist-oriented Cuba, but it is certain that the Kremlin is giving this possibility the closest consideration.

Apart from these stationary bases, Russia has, of course, for many years been using some vessels of her fishing fleets as floating supply stations. The expansion of the submarine fleet demanded the training of ever-increasing crews and caused the number of annual long-distance exercise cruises to be doubled from year to year. These cruises have, in fact, gone as far as Newfoundland and Alaska. Russian submarines and fishing trawlers, however, are prowling the world's seas for much more than training purposes or fish hunts.

Citing intelligence reports, Representative Daniel J. Flood of Pennsylvania testified before the House Defense Appropriations Subcommittee in May, 1961: "We have information of their great whaling fleets. There is not a square foot of the water of the world that some Russian ship, or boat of some kind, has not been operating in for years and years and years since the war. They are now moving into every nook and cranny they can get into. . . . They are allegedly shipping and fishing. There are these whaling fleets. All contain, without any question, special survey teams for oceanography and hydrography."

And, according to Admiral John T. Hayward, it is also very likely that the Soviet Union is mapping the New England coastal waters in detail through its trawler fleet and submarines.

According to Western experts, all this work will provide the Soviets by 1966–67 with an exact map of the ocean floor and a key to the various conditions prevailing in the deep sea—factors of the utmost strategic importance.

Originally the sea bed was surveyed only in those frequently used, shallow waters near the coast. Underwater obstacles thus encountered could be entered on charts and the best routes for coastal voyages ascertained. In World War II, for example, the U.S. Navy had first of all to find a couple of Alaskan fishermen who knew the waters around the Aleutian Islands so that some warships could be piloted there to smoke out the Japanese forces at Kiska and Attu.

Even today the knowledge of the sea and its floor in our possession reaches no further than a hundred miles from the coast, and American oceanographers reckon that even here our knowledge is incomplete. Precise maps of the sea floor, however, are vital to every submarine commander. Since he may be forced to remain submerged for days or even weeks, all underwater "landmarks" can help him to determine his exact position in the ocean. Without such information, his military mission may become a suicidal adventure, comparable to driving a ten-ton truck blindfolded over a highway.

So far the West neither knows the exact location of the best submarine attack routes, nor does it have the means of blocking them securely once they have been found.

This has led experts like Admiral Thach to talk of a "hole in America's defense curtain." While the powerful radar towers of the Distant Early Warning Line and the Ballistic Missile Early Warning System can spot approaching bombers and intercontinental missiles, there is still no effective operational protection against the invisible enemy in the sea.

It took British and American frigates, submarines and airplanes almost a week to find the Portuguese ocean liner *Santa María* after she was seized by political adventurers in January of 1961. They vainly searched the surface for this relatively large ship, though they knew its approximate position. How much harder, then, will it be to find a tiny submarine somewhere deep in the ocean.

With the nuclear submarines being built in this country

since 1952, the United States hopes to meet the rising danger imposed by the Red fleet. Not only do nuclear-powered submarines possess more speed and striking power than conventional submarines and thus provide an effective deterrent, but they can cruise the high seas almost indefinitely without the need of returning to their base every three months or so.

Submarine crews, it is said, fear nothing more than being tracked by an enemy submarine. In such a case they lose their supreme advantages of invisibility and surprise attack. Instead of being able to attack they have to be on the defensive. Admiral Momsen gave a perfect description of the situation: "Two hostile submarines under water are like two duelists in the dark armed with baseball bats. Each one is waiting for the other to strike first so that he may reveal his position."

The more heavily one of the duelists is armed, the more his opponent will fear to strike the first blow. The aim of the new American submarines is to deter every enemy right from the start. Thanks to their almost inexhaustible supply of energy their radius of action is practically unlimited. The *Nautilus*, the first vessel developed under the guidance and supervision of (then) Captain Hyman Rickover in 1952, covered sixty thousand nautical miles before her atom reactor had to be refueled.

This spic-and-span boat, equipped with red leather seats, linoleum floors and a large, fairly comfortable mess hall, is to a certain extent the ancestor of the U.S. nuclear submarine fleet. Quite a number of atomic subs of varying shape and astonishing capabilities have been developed, based on experience gained with the *Nautilus*. Among the more impressive are: the *Seawolf* (3,200 tons), which cruised under water for sixty days with 116 men on board and without having to surface even once; the *Skipjack*, commissioned in 1959, was then the fastest submarine in the world, ostensibly capable of traveling at 45 mph. This is faster than the speed limit on many automobile highways, or several times the speed of submarines in World War II. When it was launched there was not a destroyer in the world capable of catching up with the *Skipjack*. It can glide away from any hostile ship without effort.

This incredible speed was made possible because the engineers of the Electric Boat Division of the General Dynamics Corporation gave the boat a shape which deviated sharply from that of all other submarines previously built, and which has set the pattern for nuclear subs to come.

Boats using conventional power have a hull designed primarily for surface cruising. They are long, narrow, with sharp bows and a flat deck. Nuclear submarines, however, are meant to travel chiefly, if not exclusively, under water. This is a region where vessels with the so-called teardrop shape, first tested in the nonnuclear *Albacore*, attain the greatest speed. On the outside the *Skipjack* looks like a whale or a blimp. Its cross section is almost a perfect circle. It does not even possess a flat deck.

The conning tower, thin and streamlined, carries two horizontal rudders which act as stabilizers during submarine voyages. Actually a journey beneath the waves is smoother than a trip in the observation car of a passenger train. But in an emergency the *Skipjack* can be as maneuverable as a sports plane. It goes into a turn at an angle of 33°, and can make a complete turn in an incredibly narrow circle. All maneuvers are executed by a helmsman, as in an airplane, with the aid of a joy stick.

But even these astonishing properties have already been surpassed. In August, 1961, the Navy launched the U.S.S. *Thresher*, lead ship of the world's most advanced class of undersea craft. It will be able to dive deeper, travel faster and run more quietly than any other submarine.

"In this ship," Vice-Admiral Harold T. Deutermann, Chief of Staff to the Supreme Commander of NATO, said during the launching ceremony, "we see gathered for the first time the marvelous energy of nuclear power, the evolutionary development of submarine hull forms—begun in *Albacore*, tested and refined in *Skipjack* and her sisters, and epitomized in *Thresher*. We see a weapons system so advanced in concept and design that no other submarine in the world today can equal her range and fire power for antisubmarine weapons. We see the inclusion of a sonar system so sensitive and so powerful that the ocean around her for greater distances than ever before becomes her territory."

Whereas the *Thresher* belongs to the class of killer submarines, the *Triton* can be considered an underwater laboratory and reconnaissance ship.

When launched in 1959, it was considered the largest underwater vessel in the world. But it can hardly be called a submarine any more. With its two atomic power plants, three decks and crew of 172, the *Triton* is more of an underwater ship. This 440-foot-long craft with a water displacement of 5,900 tons equals a coastal freighter in size.

The *Triton*, equipped with extensive radar and sonar devices, is already cruising the seas on a constant lookout for suspicious vessels on or beneath the water. It is continually informed of other submarines' operations and virtually represents a floating mobile and submersible headquarters. The "combat room," from which all operations are conducted, resembles the control center of a good-sized airport: illuminated plastic maps form the walls, radar and sonar screens present an electronic picture of all objects in "inner" and "outer" space and could make this electronic laboratory an oceanographer's dream. Its radius of operation is close to 110,000 miles. Food provisions on board are sufficient for the crew for several months. When the *Triton* surfaced in May, 1960, after an underwater voyage of eighty-four days, members of the crew declared: "It was a routine trip."

But the real counterbalance to Russia's submarines—though not a defense against them—and even to her intercontinental ballistic missiles, is represented by an entirely new class of American submarine. Its boats, in a way, represent a fusion of modern missile techniques with the science of nuclear ship propulsion. The vessels were developed to cruise in the depths of the oceans as highly mobile, but primarily as invisible, missile bases. These are the boats of the FBM—Fleet of Ballistic Missile submarines, better known as Polaris subs.

As early as 1950 U.S. Navy missilemen had recommended the construction of missile-carrying submarines to the U.S. government. They claimed that "against a waterborne missile there is no defense, and the Administration would be well advised to have it." But it was not easy to implement this recommendation. At that time, there was no type of submarine capable of carrying large, long-range missiles, nor any type of underwater missile which could be fired from a submarine.

By 1955 it was finally decided to modify the American Jupiter-type IRBM so that it could be launched from a submarine. But the dangers to be coped with were great—almost too great. Liquid-fuel rockets are as malicious as jackals; they are also complicated and unreliable. Should only a single one misfire during a launching from a submarine, the boat could be torn to pieces. The difficulties appeared insurmountable until, precisely at the right moment, a group of chemists made a discovery which saved the day for the project. They developed a new and sufficiently powerful solid fuel. With it, a relatively safe propellant became available, equal in performance to liquid fuels, but without the latter's disadvantages.

After a short period of consideration a decision was then reached: instead of modifying the Jupiter liquid-fueled missile, Navy scientists were to develop an entirely new missile, driven by a solid propellant. This was the birth of the Polaris. It was also the birth of a new fleet of submarines equipped with Polaris missiles, the manufacture of which has received highest priority since 1959.

The U.S. Navy estimated late in 1961 that a total of fifty of these boats, fully equipped, would permit a constant number of them to be on continuous patrol in all waters, just as atom bombers of the Strategic Air Command are constantly in the air. In January, 1962, six Polaris subs were in commission, an additional twenty-three were being built or on order, and by mid-1963 one such ship should be completed every month.

Captain C. H. Meigs of the Navy's Special Projects Office explained on December 2, 1959, that the advantage of the Polaris system is its ability to reach "almost any point—certainly all the important industrial centers in the Eurasian Continent—from one of the surrounding seas."

What do these American missile submarines look like? Let us, for instance, consider the *George Washington*, the first Polaris craft, launched in June of 1959. It was originally to bear the name *Scorpion* and was intended to be the sister ship of the *Skipjack*. But as the work on Polaris missiles was progressing so well, the Navy decided to cut the half-finished boat in two and insert a middle section for missiles. The *Scorpion*'s flat nose and most of her maneuverability remained, but not her high speed.

The missile room is situated in the 118-foot-long center section directly behind the conning tower in the front third of the boat. The crew call it "Sherwood Forest," because in the shimmering green light of the boat sixteen green-painted missile tubes rise like tree trunks from the linoleum-covered floor. Each contains one of the 28-foot, 28,000-pound Polaris missiles. This room alone carries a well-spread-out weight of 224 tons, which could be doubled if necessary.

The compressed air for launching the missiles from under water is contained in strong, plastic tanks, weighing over a ton each. When the firing button is pressed a part of this compressed air ejects the individual missile, which weighs as much as a truck, sixty feet above the water! Only then does the engine ignite to push the two-stage missile high into the stratosphere. With its H-bomb warhead, more destructive than the Hiroshima and Nagasaki atom bombs, it rises four hundred miles into space. Then it storms toward its target twelve to fifteen hundred miles away.

On the fifteenth of November, 1960, the sub, now renamed *George Washington*, set off from Charleston, South Carolina, her hull loaded with deadly projectiles sufficient to transform sixteen cities of Moscow's size into smoking rubble. Her destination was kept strictly secret and can only be guessed, but her patrol area will be within range of the Soviet targets she would be expected to destroy if nuclear war broke out. Immediately after the boat's departure, more than a hundred Soviet fishing boats assembled in the Norwegian Sea. One can be sure that they were not there solely for the purpose of fishing.

With her three decks and a displacement of 6,700 tons when submerged, the *George Washington* equals a light cruiser in size. It is the first submarine to have two crews, Blue and Gold, each comprising ninety men and ten officers, who relieve each other after every voyage. In this way the boat is continuously in action, apart from the few hours when it returns to its base in Holy Loch, Scotland, every sixty days for a change of crew. "Men get worn out quicker than machines—at least they do in a nuclear submarine," observed James B. Osborn, captain of the Blue crew.

Rear Admiral William F. Raborn, Jr., testified before the House Space Committee in July of 1959 that there are "no significant military targets . . . that cannot be brought under fire" by the *Polaris*. "It [the missile] is one of the most attractive deterrents we have in our bag of tricks. If war comes, of course, it will have failed its first purpose, to serve as a deterrent. But in the event of war, every submarine at sea becomes a potential Polaris carrier."

By the end of 1960 the *Patrick Henry*, the second boat of

the new Polaris fleet, was on her way through the depths, and in the spring of 1962 a total of six such boats were stationed within rocket range of Russia, bringing the number of possible targets that could be wiped out with one blow to ninety-six. They represent our highest trump card in the Berlin "pressure game."

But even more is planned for the deep sea. In 1961, tests are being conducted with a new, improved version of the Polaris which will have a range of up to 1,700 miles. The eventual target is Polaris missiles with a range of 2,800 to 2,900 miles, to be fired from the larger Polaris submarines of the *Ethan Allen* class. Once our boats are equipped with such missiles there will be no ocean large enough to ensure the safety of a hostile target.

Since the spring of 1960 the U.S. Navy has also been experimenting with firing even larger missiles from the sea, simply by hanging them vertically, nose up, between buoys. The water serves as a cheap, relatively safe and virtually indestructible launching platform. Frigate Captain John E. Drain, who developed this method of launching (called Project Hydra I), is confident that it will one day be possible to fire manned moon rockets weighing two hundred tons this way. A further possibility, he says, is a chain of hard-to-locate missile bases placed over a wide area of the ocean floor.

It is indeed thought that the American missile submarine underwater bases will cause a change in the whole American defense policy. The battleground of an eventual war may shift from land to sea. In the future, all missile bases may perhaps be transferred to the depths of the oceans, making it senseless for any enemy to try a surprise attack on the North American Continent. An annihilating counterblow from well-hidden missile submarines would immediately follow such an act. Every single submarine of the Polaris type carries missiles in its belly whose combined destructive power is greater than that of all bombs that were dropped in World War II by all participating nations.

And the fact that about 335 million cubic miles of ocean water protect a missile-carrying submarine of the nuclear-powered type makes it difficult to destroy it and almost impossible to blow up the entire fleet at the same time. This is what makes advocates of the Polaris system confident that a sufficient number of boats will ensure the preservation of world peace. "We sometimes forget," said Admiral Charles R. Brown, Commander of Allied Forces Southern Europe, "that the Russians themselves can be scared, too."

The performance and significance of the new nuclear-powered submarines are so great compared with the conservative diesel-powered vessels that other seafaring nations outside Russia have also started building nuclear-powered submarines.

On the twenty-first of October, 1960, the first British "Sub-Killer" to be driven by atomic power was launched to hunt its enemy counterpart. The *Dreadnought*, designed on the lines of the *Skipjack*, had power installations which came from America. The Dutch Navy is also planning an atomic submarine, as are France, Italy and West Germany.

In addition, the United States in December of 1960 offered NATO five submarines armed with eighty Polaris missiles to be delivered before the end of 1963. But building a strong fleet of missile-carrying submarines, even within the framework of NATO, is not enough.

Until we develop effective detecting apparatus and anti-submarine weapons, it will be impossible for us to defend ourselves against enemy attack originating in the oceans.

Progress Through Fear

Fear brings progress in its wake. The construction of submarines involves mainly technical and physical problems, but
for an effective defense against submarines specifically oceanographic questions and phenomena must be explained. In the
spring of 1959 the United States together with eight NATO
countries—England, West Germany, Italy, France, Nether-
lands, Norway, Denmark and Canada—established an international scientific research center in the Italian port of La
Spezia, whose purpose is to solve all problems connected with
the detection and warding off of submarines.

Closer to our own shores is the so-called AUTEC—for
Atlantic Underwater Test and Evaluation Center—which the
Navy is currently building at Great Exuma, one of the
Bahama Islands. One of the major objectives of this new center
will be to test detection systems and other devices used in
antisubmarine warfare (ASW). Among these are testing
facilities for various torpedoes and new types of underwater
missiles. Both these centers represent a combined effort to
solve a variety of problems. There are, of course, smaller
projects which concentrate on only one oceanographic phenomenon.

There can be little doubt that the results of La Spezia,
Great Exuma and other projects precipitated by anxiety about
security will eventually produce not only better protection

against enemy submarines, but also the answers to many oceanographic questions whose solution might otherwise have escaped us for years to come.

For example, to render submarine defense effective, it would be valuable to know how deep sunlight penetrates into the lower regions of the sea, a question of burning interest to marine biologists for many years. A thorough survey of the sea bed to a depth of three thousand feet is at present also being made. Furthermore, it must be ascertained whether any natural sounds occur at great depths, like those emitted by fish in shallower waters. This would chiefly interest sonar experts, and be useful to oceanographers in classifying the different "voices." It will enable the "language" of fish to be learned more quickly than had been possible before. Another vital question is what effect the pressure at great depths has on mechanical instruments such as the different kinds of measuring apparatus outside a diving vessel or on the shutters of torpedo tubes in future deep-sea ships.

Finally, one of the most urgent problems to which experts from the nations represented at La Spezia, and our scientists at Great Exuma, are seeking a solution is the behavior of sound under water. Sound travels five times more swiftly in water than it does in air. But how far does it travel? It has been established that there are "sound channels" in the sea, where noises carry extraordinarily well for distances of thousands of miles. The American oceanographer Professor Maurice Ewing was so fascinated by this phenomenon that he delivered a special lecture on the subject to the U.S. Navy shortly before the Second World War, but he was not given much of a hearing. Seven years passed before the U.S. Navy decided, in the summer of 1944, to go into the matter. And sure enough, the explosion of a few pounds of dynamite at a depth of a thousand feet off Pearl Harbor, Hawaii, could be heard distinctly off San Diego at the same depth, some 2,500 miles away. Another small charge detonated in the Indian Ocean could be picked up by underwater microphones in the Atlantic not far from New York, nine thousand miles away.

Based on these observations, a modern method for "signal" transmission was developed into the so-called SOFAR (Sound Fixing and Ranging) communications method. When astronaut Alan Shepard landed in the South Atlantic after his suborbital flight, one of the signaling devices aboard his space capsule was a small detonator, developed especially on the SOFAR principle.

If "lost," Shepard was to drop the "bomb" into the water. At a predetermined depth it would detonate, enabling Navy search and rescue ships to get a "fix" on the exact position of the detonation. It is planned to include similar detonators in the survival equipment of all Air Force and Navy pilots who may have to bail out over the sea.

According to oceanographer Columbus Iselin of Woods Hole, "There isn't an ocean in the world big enough to lose the sound of a pistol shot fired at the right depth." This became even more evident in March, 1960, when a sound channel was discovered that extends halfway round the earth over a distance of twelve thousand miles. American scientists on board the research ship *Vema* let off some detonations at a certain water depth not far from the Australian coast. For some time the sound waves traveled very close to the surface, rounded the Cape of Good Hope, sank to a depth of about 2,560 feet near the Equator and after 223 minutes reached the SOFAR station on the island of Bermuda.

There is a sound channel similar to the one between Hawaii and California in the uppermost three thousand feet of the Atlantic. Many of these peculiar zones exist year in, year out in some seas, while others shift periodically. Their existence, as well as the quality of sound transmission through the water, depends on the salinity of the water and the temperature, but the precise factors are still unknown. One of the purposes of Project Nekton was to uncover the mysteries of these channels.

"This is vital for us," declared an American oceanographer, "for without an exact knowledge of the behavior of sound waves under water the whole of our submarine defense is useless."

The peculiar behavior of sound under water continues to be a headache for U.S. antisubmarine warfare. Although many of these problems arose before World War II, not all of them have as yet been satisfactorily solved. In the latter months of 1939, for instance, the U.S. submarine defense was alerted when hydrophones (underwater microphones) picked up a series of unusual noises. The hydrophone operators believed them to "come from unidentified submarines." An investigation, however, proved them to be no more than a school of squeaking porpoises.

Oceanographers, called to the aid of the Navy, taught the hydrophone crews that not all underwater noises come from submarines. The sea is by no means the "silent world" it has often been designated. It is rather filled with countless, mysterious sounds. The difficulty, in spite of thorough training, is to identify them properly. Thus some American submarine hunters pursued what they supposed to be a foreign sub for four days in 1958. They finally discovered to their disillusion that they had been following a school of fish.

A similar incident which even caused worldwide headlines occurred more recently along the coast of South America. "The mysterious submarine supposed to have entered the heavily guarded Gulf of Nuevo in February, 1960, according to reports by the Argentine Navy, never existed at all," explained Edward Beach, skipper of the *Triton*, in a press conference three months after the event. "It was actually nothing more than a multitude of fish."

With the variety of sea sounds one of the present tasks therefore is to examine and classify them. Hydrophones not only pick up various underwater fish sounds, but also, of course, the noise of the propellers emitted by the vessel to be detected. They also pick up sounds like the coughing of a crew member in an enemy submarine, the buzzing of batteries or the clash of metal. This "passive sound detection" was first introduced in World War I to locate German submarines. Until recently, identification of the sound was entirely up to the individual operator. Obviously, modern electronic devices should be able to do the same job much faster and with greater accuracy.

For this purpose the Sperry Gyroscope Company has erected a miniature ocean on its grounds to test submarine detection apparatus. It consists of a large basin 400 feet by 200 feet and 25 feet deep, filled with sea water. By electronic means all the possible known noises of the sea, besides that of a submarine, can be reproduced: the squealing of a whale, which sounds like someone opening a door with rusty hinges; the light humming of eels, similar to a boiling teakettle; and the noise made by a school of shrimps, which sounds like the sizzling of an egg in the frying pan. Against this background new instruments are being developed to ignore or filter out automatically all the "wrong" sounds and indicate only the noise of a submarine.

Admiral Thach once said: "Like Tarzan in the jungle, we have to learn to distinguish the friendly sounds from the hostile ones—the monkeys from the tigers!" The victor in this game of "blind man's buff," as one authority described it, will be the one with the most sensitive hearing.

But despite recent advances we are still a long way from perfecting this means of passive submarine detection.

Fortunately, shortly before and during World War II a means for "active" detection of enemy submarines was developed. This SONAR (for Sound Navigation and Ranging) proved so successful that it more than anything else helped to destroy the German submarine fleet. Losing at first only one U-boat for every sixteen Allied ships they sent to the bottom, by 1944 the Germans had to pay with one submarine for every single ship that they destroyed.

The active sonar system is based on the principle that underwater sound waves bounce back when they hit a target and can be measured in a manner similar to radar on the surface.

To the distress of submarine chasers the active sonar method works only under good water conditions. This, up to now, has made a one hundred percent successful detection method impossible. Among the problems facing sonar experts, for instance, are the phenomena of "warm-water pockets" and the "phantom bottom." Representatives of the U.S., Brazilian and Argentinian navies believe that it is not the search for fish which continually brings Russian submarines near the coasts of North and South America, but rather the search for these pockets. The sea is made up of water layers of varying temperatures gradually decreasing as we move toward the bottom. Where the temperature difference between the surface layer and that immediately below is greater than normal, a so-called "warm-water pocket" is formed, which is extremely dangerous for any nation threatened by submarines. Such pockets were discovered by mere chance just before the Second World War.

On that occasion an American destroyer was testing a new active sonar device in the waters off Cuba. Until that trial voyage everything had gone off beautifully. The apparatus had indicated submarines under water and the experienced crew had been able to fix the distance and exact location of every submarine by the "ping-ping" of the returning echo. But in the waters around Cuba the sonar gear began to behave most peculiarly. All at once it indicated so many targets that the crew got completely confused. The sound waves were thrown back by targets later found to be nonexistent. A submarine was then sent down as a test decoy. The sonar apparatus failed completely to take the bearings of the submarine. In a real emergency, it would have been assumed that there was nothing there and the crew would have felt perfectly safe.

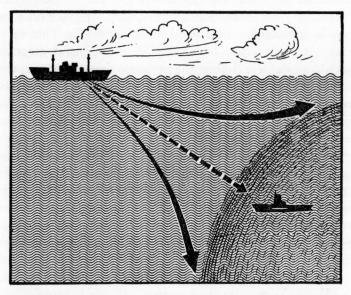

As water is a bad conductor of heat, cold and warm layers of water can lie next to each other without uniting. The sound waves of a sonar apparatus are deflected at the meeting of two such layers instead of penetrating further; a submarine beyond this boundary remains concealed.

Once again the Navy called the oceanographers to their aid, turning to the then new institute at Woods Hole which immediately sent experts to Cuba. The expedition, under the direction of Dr. Iselin, soon ascertained the reasons for the sonar malfunction. The oceanographers discovered great variations of temperature in the water. A layer of water, extending fifty feet below the surface like a big pocket, was much warmer than the water immediately beneath it. At the boundary between warm and cold water an invisible "wall" had formed. The impulses of the sonar were reflected as if they had hit a solid obstacle instead of continuing in a straight path. Any submarine could thus hide beneath the pocket and avoid being discovered.

Based on this observation oceanographers invented a bathythermograph which gives temperature readings to a depth of several hundred feet. With it, temperature changes at various depths can be read off instantaneously. During the Second World War, U.S. submarines equipped with such instruments were able to track down a warm-water pocket when pursued by the sonar of German, Italian or Japanese destroyers, and hide there until the danger had passed.

It is known that modern Russian submarines are fitted with bathythermographs and that they systematically collect information about these warm-water pockets on extensive voyages. Though the number and distribution of such pockets often vary, according to season, weather, region or even time of day, one thing is obvious: The more one naval power knows about these warm-water pockets, the more it will benefit.

We know that some of these underwater hiding places lie off the East Coast of America where the Gulf Stream flows. Another lies in the Pacific near the strategically important Panama Canal, and yet another area extends down the 25° latitude near the intersection with the Tropic of Cancer. Besides warm-water pockets, this area contains certain magnetic anomalies which make it difficult to locate submarines with the aid of detecting devices normally sensitive to the magnetism of the submarine's steel mass. U.S. submarines have therefore been engaged in mapping the ocean floor around the United States for the past two years, hoping to discover the most favorable approaches for enemy missile submarines planning to attack the U.S. Although much of the most modern sonar equipment aboard American destroyers has a range of thirty miles, the impulses are often returned by temperature boundaries only a few hundred yards away. As late as 1961, Admiral Thach considered all Western sonar apparatus unsatisfactory.

One further vital task for oceanographers in La Spezia and Great Exuma will be to solve the mystery of the "deep scattering layer" or "D.S.L." Working from surface ships, investigators would have been able to give no satisfactory explanation of this peculiar ocean phenomenon. It was first discovered in World War II off the coast of California. In certain places it was impossible to obtain accurate records of deep waters with the aid of echo sounders. Even though Navy men engaged in the work were certain that the depth at a given spot was, for example, nine hundred fathoms, the graphs of their echo sounders gave readings of only six hundred or four hundred or even three hundred fathoms. Something like a "phantom bottom" must be preventing the signals from reaching the actual bottom. Were this phantom bottom close to the surface, a submarine could easily hide beneath it.

Once again the Navy called upon the oceanographers for help. This time even the scientists were perplexed. However much they searched, they found neither promontories, forests of seaweed nor other large obstacles. Neither could the phantom bottom be caused by schools of fish, as the area where it had been observed covered some three hundred square miles.

Gradually, more reports of similar observations began to come in at Navy headquarters. "Phantom bottoms"—subsequently called "scattering layers"—were soon detected in all ocean waters, including those of the Arctic and Antarctic. Some of them were as thick as two hundred feet. What is more, it was found that they usually rise toward the surface at night and, before sunrise, migrate toward deeper waters. On a voyage across the Pacific the U.S.S. *Nereus* found places where as many as two such layers, each reacting differently to daybreak, lay one above the other.

It is now generally assumed—based on the latest work by marine biologists—that scattering layers are formed by minute forms of marine life. They may be either plankton, shrimps, fish or squid, but in such quantities as to repulse the sound of the echo sounder. One is reminded of the tinfoil strips which Allied bombers dropped over German cities in order to confuse the radar defenses.

Significant as the discovery of scattering layers may be, it is a phenomenon unwelcome to those concerned with antisubmarine warfare. Its great advantage to hiding submarines is that as soon as dusk falls they can climb from a depth of a thousand feet to within a few feet of the surface, remaining concealed all the while under this scattering layer.

As early as 1959 the CIA reported that Russian submarines were already systematically gathering information about the distribution of the scattering layers, whereas the Americans didn't even know with certainty how they were formed. No wonder, therefore, that Admiral Arleigh Burke expressed this opinion when asked about submarine detection: "I am satisfied neither with the ability of the U.S. Navy to protect the Atlantic and Pacific seaways, nor with our antisubmarine warfare. If we were certain of being able to locate all submarines within a radius of twenty to thirty miles and identify them as friend or foe, then we could be satisfied."

Though they may appear scanty, instruments and defense units have been developed in America since 1945 which would fill every old submariner with respect. Three United States' HUKFOR groups are continuously ready for action in the Atlantic and Pacific: Task Groups Alpha, Bravo and Charlie. HUKFOR is the abbreviation for Hunter-Killer Force, the official name for the antisubmarine warfare groups. At present, they serve the U.S. Navy as laboratories for new detection and counteroffensive devices.

Pacific Task Group Alpha, for instance, five thousand men strong, consists of the aircraft carrier *Valley Forge*, eight destroyers, two submarines and one squadron each of Grumman S2F submarine chasers and helicopters. Like the other HUKFOR groups, it is equipped with the most modern depth charges and torpedoes. They are a far cry from the early torpedoes of World War II, the firing of which had more or less to rely on guesswork. Today's torpedoes do not have to be aimed. They "home in" on an enemy sub. If they work on the acoustical principle, they follow the sound of its propellers. If based on the infrared principle, they can detect the heat of its nuclear reactor or diesel engine. And if detonated by magnetic fuses, they will themselves seek out the metal hull of the enemy submarine.

Most of America's modern torpedoes can be launched by airplanes, fired by surface craft or by submarines. Some of them, like Asroc and Subroc, are even a combination missile-torpedo type. Subroc, for instance, is fired like a missile, flies some forty to fifty miles, then dives into the water close to the suspected sub and lies in wait. Its built-in sonar equipment picks up the noise of the enemy and directs the torpedo missile toward the vessel. Only then does the nuclear warhead explode.

Even more powerful are two nuclear depth charges with the whimsical names of Lulu and Betty. While the conventional depth charge in the Second World War had a blasting effect over a radius of about a hundred yards, the destructive power of Lulu and Betty extends over several thousand yards, enough to blow up the nine hundred largest vessels of the U.S. Navy simultaneously, if they were ever anchored together at one spot.

One has to remember, however, that many of the modern homing torpedoes of the HUKFOR are based on the work done by the Germans toward the end of World War II. It is likely, therefore, that the Russians themselves, with the capture of Peenemünde and other German research centers, gained a lot of knowledge on advanced antisubmarine weapons. Furthermore, their espionage of Western submarine and antisubmarine weapons is massive and intense. As late as February, 1961, a spy in London was accused of having sent secrets of the Royal Navy's most advanced antisubmarine devices to Moscow.

The Navy is convinced that Betty and Lulu will be able to cope with any maritime enemy. This sounds very comforting, but the hope is rather premature, as a submarine has to be located before it can be rendered impotent. For this very reason, vessels of HUKFOR are constantly sounding large parts of the Atlantic and Pacific in maneuvers, war plays and regular missions with sensitive surface and underwater detection devices. Even in peacetime they make every effort to track down Russian submarines, hoping to demonstrate to the Kremlin that they can both detect and "hold" their subs. In an interview, Rear Admiral Robert J. Stroh, leader of Task Force Bravo, said: "If we find one, we'll stay on top of him until we exhaust him. Then, we'll just dip our hat and say hello. If he submerges again, we'll stay on top of him again."

At the time of this writing, the Americans have never been able to "hold" Russian submarines—but allegedly the Russians have done it a few times to our own boats. Even if America's HUKFOR groups were able to "stay on top" of some Soviet submarines, the difficulty would still be to "hold" and thus destroy all of them in the shortest possible time.

One of the most important aspects of antisubmarine warfare is the investigation of the maximum area in the minimum time —in other words, before a submarine can fire its rockets. This is hardly possible with today's destroyers, for as soon as they reach full speed the noise of their own screws interferes with the working of their sonars.

One alternative was to use airplanes, but winged aircraft proved to be too fast. Helicopters are now employed, taking off from the deck of one of the aircraft carriers of each HUKFOR group. Each helicopter carries a new, lightweight, long-range sonar which is part of the DDD (Dip-Detect-Destroy) system. Weighing only 725 pounds and with a range of ten thousand yards, it is comparable to shipboard sonar weighing several thousand pounds.

Helicopters can thus scan hundreds of nautical miles for enemy submarines in a considerably shorter time than destroyers could.

In a simulated attack by the foe each helicopter of a HUKFOR group searches an area. The pilot descends close to the waves at certain intervals and dunks the buoy-shaped sonar suspended from a cable. This method also permits the sonar buoy to be lowered below the thermal layer of a warm-water pocket. If it spots an object, it indicates on a screen in the cockpit the direction and depth of that object. If it is identified as a hostile submarine, the pilot drops sound-sensitive "bloodhound" rockets from the helicopter. These acoustical torpedoes automatically find their way to the submarine. Early in 1960 the U.S. Navy started mass-producing the new DDD equipment.

It must not be overlooked that the Russians possess a similar instrument; in fact, they employ it not only in submarine detection but also in deep-sea fishing. With the aid of helicopters, "scouts" hurry ahead of the fishing fleet and find the position, size and direction of a school of fish. One such device was picked up by a Norwegian trawler in the Barents Sea.

Obviously, military inventions can be put to peaceful uses. The most modern, long-range sonar gear, now used chiefly to locate submarines, will one day be employed in high-seas fishing. It will not only increase the catch, but also eliminate days of searching for fish. Drifting buoys that function automatically, such as those developed in 1959 under the code name of Jezebel to locate submarines, will also be part of this search.

J. J. Coop, a physicist at the U.S. Naval Development Center in Johnsville, Pennsylvania, explained that Jezebel would enable a single aircraft to sound an area of 32,000 square miles in the sea within ten hours, a rate undreamed of heretofore.

A cargo plane can transport several hundred of these miniature, five-pound buoys, which are let down by parachutes at twenty-five- to fifty-mile intervals. Each buoy contains tiny microphones which pick up every sound made by fish and sea mammals, but especially by submarines. A tiny transmitter then sends them to individual speedboats with extremely accurate receivers. There the sounds are identified, co-ordinated and the hunt can begin, at present for submarines, one day perhaps for herring, tuna or cod.

The new buoys are the first also to radio information about the temperature measured in their respective areas. They obtain their energy from long-life batteries, though experiments are being conducted with small generators which will be powered by a pair of paddles moved up and down by the ocean swell. The sonar buoys could thus function uninterruptedly for years.

Another great step in the development of active sonar was made in November, 1960. The U.S. Navy, it was announced, was testing an advanced sonar that could detect submerged submarines at a range of thirty miles or more. Rear Admiral Lloyd M. Mustin, special assistant for antisubmarine warfare to Admiral Arleigh Burke, predicted that the advanced equipment might reach as far as seventy miles. In addition, it was also expected to penetrate the thermal layers under which, as we have already observed, enemy submarines like to hide.

The new sonar is a tremendous improvement over World War II active sonar devices, the most powerful of which had a range of only two to three miles. The new device, called the Artemis, is far heavier and more cumbersome than its predecessors. Basically, it consists of a monstrous transducer, an instrument that creates and emits sound under water.

So much electrical power is needed to manufacture the sound that it would be enough to supply a city of fifty thousand people. The fifty-foot-long transducer, weighing several hundred tons, and all the power-generating equipment had to be mounted on a seventeen-thousand-ton tanker, the *Mission Capistrano*.

As soon as the transducer is lowered into the water it starts to emit low-frequency sound waves of enormous power. This sound, with the pitch of a low piano note, travels great distances under water. If the sound waves, radiating from the mammoth transducer in all directions, hit any underwater object, they bounce back. A chain of hydrophones, placed by the Navy in various parts of the Atlantic, picks up this reflected sound—and with it all other underwater noises. The signals of all hydrophones are relayed through underwater cables to a seventy-six-foot tower off the Bermudas.

The tower, known as Argus Island, stands atop an extinct volcano in the ocean. It contains a vast array of electronic equipment, computers and sound analyzers, as well as accommodations for the service crew. Here the signals picked up by all the hydrophones are fed into computing machines. Once the system is completed, Navy officials hope that electronic brains will then be able to distinguish which sound stems from a whale off Cape Cod, which from a school of porpoises off Florida, and which from a fleet of unidentified submarines heading toward Cape Hatteras.

Artemis may become the underwater equivalent of the North American radar warning system. It may be able to detect submarines in all the open seas of the world and under the ice of the Arctic Ocean. (Naturally, the Soviets may try to build a similar monster of detection, to seek out America's Polaris-carrying submarines. But it is believed that submarine detection is a field where the Russians still lag far behind.)

Meanwhile, until Artemis becomes operational (and no one can tell for sure how soon this will be) other means of detection have to be perfected. One of them is a "sniff" device, fixed to low-flying patrol planes, which will react to samples of air polluted by the diesel exhaust gases of submarines.

Another possibility is television cameras operating in the weakest light or able to see several thousand yards in the dark to be put aboard coastal defense vessels and defensive submarines. The General Electric Company already has developed such an instrument, which can transmit in the dark clear pictures of objects which could never be detected by the naked human eye.

In addition, there are infrared instruments able to detect an enemy submarine over great distances from the heat it radiates. In 1959 the U.S. Air Force produced a camera which could take almost ghostly-looking photographs in which the silhouettes of cars and ships could be recognized quite clearly. At the time the photographs were taken, there were no cars in the parking lots nor ships on the waterways; they had left some hours before. What the camera had caught was the heat the cars and ships had left behind.

The Americans are working on another instrument which bears the name MAD, an abbreviation of Magnetic Detection. Installed in an aircraft, it informs the crew immediately should the plane fly over a metal body in the water, even if it lies hundreds of feet deep. Unfortunately, the sunken object could just as easily be a wreck as a submarine. For this reason many HUKFOR experts believe that the Russians have selected as one of their approaches the route around Cape Hatteras, the "graveyard of the Atlantic," where locating with MAD equipment is much less efficient. Unfortunately, too, the horizontal radius of action of this locating device is very limited. The plane has to fly almost directly over the metal body.

Since the end of 1959 special emphasis has been laid on coupling these different warning mechanisms to automatic electronic indicators, each of which would be small enough to be transported by planes of the HUKFOR groups. Station and direction of the plane would be indicated by an arrow on a fluorescent screen, the position of the submarine by a circle. The pilot of the aircraft would then have only to steer the machine onto the corresponding route until the arrow rested over the circle. Sea mines, magnetic or acoustical torpedoes would achieve the rest.

Alongside these tasks of coordination, the U.S. Navy is perfecting its Project Caesar in the greatest secrecy. Basically, when completed it would be a belt of sonar equipment laid deep around the whole coastline of North America.

Though the Navy remains tight-lipped on the subject, there have been reports that dozens of delicate electronic listening devices in watertight plastic containers have already been placed on the floor of the Atlantic off the East Coast of the United States. They are to be connected by cable with coordination centers on the mainland. A similar sonar chain along the West Coast would reach up as far as the Aleutian Islands. It is estimated that a listening chain of Project Caesar can pick up any sounds emitted over a distance of three to four hundred miles off the mainland.

It was, in fact, rumored in English newspapers in October, 1960, that the United States in conjunction with Great Britain was planning to lay a chain of eavesdropping buoys straight across the Atlantic. The English Ministry of Defense refused comment. Certainly the free world will eventually have to seek protection behind some such "electronic" curtain.

The American oceanographer, Athelstan Spilhaus, predicted as early as 1951 in his article "Turn to the Sea":

> On land we have networks of radars which plot the position of all aircraft to prevent collisions and to detect intruders. It cannot be too long before we have the counterpart of these criss-crossed networks in the sea—submarine beacons radiating sound beams for the guidance of underwater craft as the lighthouse uses a light beam to guide ships on the surface. Sound receivers must be coupled together in a vast underwater spider web of millions of cables which, like our radar surveillance in the air space, can keep track continuously of normal comings and goings, yet single out any stranger in our midst. To identify friend from foe is one of the most difficult underwater problems the Navy has.

In 1960 an underwater "radar" system was being rumored in knowledgeable circles. Several American electronic firms received secret instructions from the U.S. Navy to develop an electronic fence like Project Caesar around the whole coast. But instead of listening only, the new warning net will also be designed to "see." By means of sonic scanning devices visual images of underwater objects will be produced. The shape of the image, combined with acoustical information, will help to determine more accurately whether the detected object is a submarine or merely a whale.

Oceanographers and electronic experts are being forced to tread odd paths in their efforts to improve detecting equipment. Although there is at present no shipboard sonar gear which can penetrate warm-water pockets without great expense of energy, it is hoped that a solution to this burning problem can be found by closer study of porpoises.

Ichthyologists have found that porpoises possess a built-in

sonar. It is far more sensitive than any man-made device so far. By tossing their heads to and fro they are capable of emitting up to four hundred high-frequency impulses per second. The impulses, reflected from other objects in the water, can tell them whether a fish twenty or even forty feet away is worthy prey or not. It has even been demonstrated that blindfolded porpoises in an aquarium in Miami will swim at once to a ball thrown into their pool. On behalf of the U.S. Navy, scientists hope to discover how they achieve this. The next step will then be to try to copy their sensing organ.

The U.S. Air Force has also suddenly shown a great interest in fish, hoping by their studies to improve submarine-locating equipment. The biologist Dr. Harvey E. Snavely has been examining the remarkable electrical properties of the tropical knife fish and the electric eel. "These fish," he says, "can neither see nor hear. Yet they are in a position to distinguish between friend and foe, food and waste." They live in the dark, muddy waters of South America and in the lakes and rivers of Africa. Surrounding themselves with an electrical field, they can "see," "hear" or rather feel anything that is important to them if the field is altered or disturbed in any way. Dr. Hans W. Lissman of Harvard believes that the fish can identify any intruding object from its conductivity resistance.

Another example shows how marine scientists have begun to study certain animal characteristics in search for better instruments. In the summer of 1960 even the sluggish sea turtle gained this unexpected honor.

"These creatures have amazing powers of navigation," says Archie Carr, biologist at the University of Florida. "They travel thousands of miles in the sea, yet every three years they return to the same part of the same beach to lay their eggs."

Carr believes that turtles orient themselves by the stars and swim in a straight line to where they lay their eggs. To find out more details in support of this theory Carr intends to catch several turtles on their way to Florida. He then plans to tie colored balloons to their shells and thus keep track of them by day. Small transmitters attached to the balloons will enable him to follow the turtles at night.

"I am amazed that these animals with their small brains can find their way better than man does with all his intelligence and complex instruments," says Carr enthusiastically. Based on his discoveries, he hopes to work out an improved navigation aid for our ships.

The first practical results of bionics—the name given to the study of the applicability of biological processes to mechanics and electronics—have already been achieved. Dr. Max O. Kramer, expert in fluid dynamics, has long believed that the speed-reducing eddies which form around any body moving through water could be eliminated. A close examination of porpoises showed Dr. Kramer that they have a very thin elastic outer skin which yields to any pressure. Wherever an eddy forms, the skin relaxes and weakens the eddy's braking effect. They can thus reduce all eddies to a minimum. Thereupon Dr. Kramer stuck many little foam-rubber cylinders uniformly around the hull of a model submarine, which he then covered with a smooth foam-rubber skin. The space between hull, rubber cylinders and outer skin was filled with a viscous fluid. Experiments proved clearly that the new rubber skin eliminated the braking effect of the eddies by 50 percent. Submarines of 1970 may well be equipped with such a rubber skin. Also in the pursuit of increased speed, engineers of an American shipyard have constructed "mechanical fish." They want to discover why it is that fish can move ten to twelve times faster through the water than conventional man-made vessels.

That the majority of maritime research projects are nowadays undertaken for preponderantly military reasons should cause neither surprise nor alarm in this age of the cold war.

Man will never land on the moon by 1970 if military authorities don't continually emphasize its strategic importance. It is the same with oceanography. Hardly any military invention has not brought about progress for the civilian life of a nation in one way or another. Thanks to the development of sonar, for instance, or the increased speeds of our atomic submarines, bristling though they are with weapons, sailors of 1980 will look back on what we call modern mercantile vessels with the same amused condescension that we show toward the clippers of the nineteenth century. And the fact that the navies of the world are at present looking for new underwater approaches to the coasts of a possible enemy means the first steps in establishing the routes of future merchant fleets. This development is impressively suggested by the number of recent "under ice" voyages of American nuclear submarines.

6   Waterway of the Future

At the top of our planet lies a sea touching the coasts of the great powers in the Northern Hemisphere. Yet no ship is ever seen crossing its surface, as a ten-foot layer of ice covers it in both summer and winter. Nonetheless, many experts call the Arctic Ocean the waterway of the future. The majority of mankind lives north of the Equator, and the shortest route from Seattle to India, for example, is across the Arctic Circle. Some airline companies have already acknowledged this fact by introducing polar flights. In future decades merchant ships will similarly wend their way through a new sea. Rather than crossing the Atlantic, they will choose a shorter and quicker route via the North Pole. Of course they won't have to plow through the ice—they will travel under it. The Arctic Ocean, which only a few years ago was a territory on which expeditions rarely set foot, and even then only the boldest explorers, a handful of whom returned safe and sound, will soon be accessible to all in the comfort of an easy chair deep down under the ice, well protected from the storms and bitter cold overhead.

The first thrust by the U.S. nuclear submarine *Nautilus* underneath the icecap of that frozen ocean in 1957 opened up a new era in naval transport. Its significance for future navigation and exploration of the sea is as great as the first motor-powered flight by the Wright brothers was for aviation.

Thanks to its nuclear submarines, the United States already has more information on the Arctic Ocean than any other country in the world including Russia, though in 1957, when America began an intensive investigation of the Arctic, conditions were quite the opposite. In those years, very little was known by American scientists about the geophysical, meteorological and oceanographic conditions in that area. Dr. Ernst A. Petty, Dean of the University of Alaska, complained bitterly to the Navy in Washington: "The Russians realized the great significance of the Arctic long ago. While we are spending millions on exploring the Antarctic, which is not nearly as important for us as the exploration of the Arctic, the Russians are making one North Pole expedition after the other."

Indeed, Russia organized a regular shipping service between Murmansk and eastern Siberia along the edge of the Arctic icecap as far back as the Second World War. Nowadays, too, several convoys steam through the ice every summer bringing supplies of food and fuel to Russian bases in the Arctic; they are accompanied by icebreakers and aircraft on the lookout for open waters in the ice pack which make the journey easier.

Between 1945 and 1957 Russian aircraft made hundreds of landings in Arctic regions, many just off the coast of Alaska. Their meteorological expeditions landed on numerous ice floes and some twenty other fixed points, often only 180 miles from the coast of North America. Their own sources state that by 1957 they had made well over five hundred landings in the area between Canada and northern Russia.

Until that time America had done nothing to equal these undertakings. The twenty landings made by American aircraft up to the autumn of 1957 were all exclusively on the U.S. side of the Arctic Ocean. Mostly seaplanes were used, but sometimes aircraft with skids as well. Our main undertaking was Project Skijump in 1951–52, in the course of which a twin-engined Douglas made twelve landings on large ice floes. The most important northerly point reached, however, was still 450 miles from the Pole. The aircraft was fitted with a power saw which cut holes in the ice, a power drill and a winch with a steel cable for raising samples of sea-floor deposits. On touching down for the thirteenth time, however, the landing gear was damaged and the project was abandoned. The charter planes that landed on smaller floes from then on never dared venture further than two hundred miles from the mainland.

As early as 1957, Dr. Petty warned that unless more was done in this field, the United States would lose the scientific battle of the Arctic to Russia.

When the *Nautilus* proved its worth so brilliantly on its trial voyages, he saw in the vessel an ideal oceanographic exploration ship and, as one of the first scientists, demanded a submarine expedition under the Arctic ice. "Should a submarine succeed in operating under the Arctic icecap, it would be possible to gather more information about the Arctic Ocean in a few days than has as yet been done in years," he said.

This proposal finally received the blessing of the Pentagon when they realized the strategic importance of a successful voyage under ice. They wanted to know if nuclear-powered submarines could cruise in those areas at all seasons. The *Nautilus* was to return the first answers.

In August, 1958, the boat was plowing its way through the foaming waves of the North Atlantic, headed toward the Pole. It was almost within calling distance of the diesel submarine *Trigger*, which was accompanying the *Nautilus* as far as the edge of the ice as a kind of moral support, and to give technical assistance in case of emergency.

Its nuclear-powered engines, which could operate for an almost unlimited length of time, allowed the *Nautilus* to dive under the Arctic ice. But when Lieutenant Commander William R. Anderson informed his crew of the actual destination of the project, they were somewhat taken aback. As ship's doctor R. F. Dobbins discovered, no less than 90 percent of the sailors were at first "seriously concerned" until Lieutenant Commander Cobean tried to explain by means of evening films and colored slide lectures what a voyage beneath the ice would really mean for the *Nautilus*. "Perhaps you know that most attempts to cross the Arctic Ocean by ship, or even to cut a way through, have failed. Amundsen's *Fram* was enclosed in ice for thirty-five months; yet it reached a latitude of 85° 57′. The Russian *Sedow* traveled in the ice for twenty-seven months and reached a northerly latitude of 86° 39′. We now intend to forge as far as the Pole itself. That sounds more dangerous than it probably is, for some German U-boats in World War II sought protection from Allied convoys under the edge of the Arctic icecap, which proved to be completely devoid of danger for them."

As early as 1931 an Australian, Hubert Wilkins, made an attempt to force his way through under the icecap. His own exploration in the Arctic firmly convinced Wilkins that this was possible. Conventional submarines cannot use their diesel engines when submerged, as they would eventually consume all the available oxygen. They have to resort to battery power. Wilkins planned to surface through the cracks in the ice pack, reload his batteries with the diesel engines and then dive beneath the ice for the next lap. His plan failed, not because it was impossible to carry out, but because he did not have the necessary equipment. After countless requests, the U.S. Navy "sold" him a submarine from one of its scrap yards for one dollar, on condition that he sink it when the expedition was over. Wilkins patched the holes in the hull and fitted the deck with a device which would enable him to saw his way through the ice if the batteries were to run dry prematurely.

On the way to the Arctic Wilkins lost his depth rudder. Three members of the crew are said to have sabotaged the boat out of fear of making the journey under ice. Wilkins could only force his vessel, which also happened to be called the *Nautilus*, beneath the ice with great difficulty. Then the cold compelled him to retreat. Ice was forming on the inside of the boat, the crew was freezing cold and lost courage and the bold Australian had to surrender.

"In our case," explained Cobean to the crew of the later *Nautilus*, "the temperature is always a comfortable 72° Fahrenheit. We can remain under water for an unlimited period, therefore under ice as well. Fire is the only thing which could be dangerous. But even then with our torpedoes we could shoot a hole in the icecap, surface and leave the ship. We have sufficient clothing and provisions for the Arctic climate on board. So there is no reason to be worried." But the first journey through the new sea did not turn out to be quite so smooth as Lieutenant Commander Cobean had hoped.

After eleven days both the *Nautilus* and the *Trigger* arrived at the edge of the ice. It extended unendingly to the horizon, gray-white and desolate. "Ice, ice, ice, nothing but ice," groaned sailor Burton Miller. "Boy, I'll tell you, it's going to be a drunk night when we reach England." The captains of the two boats conversed by radio. It was agreed that the *Nautilus'* first journey would take her no more than one hundred miles under the ice. Twenty hours later the boat would again meet the *Trigger* at the edge of the ice to exchange information and decide on the next steps.

It was exactly eight A.M. when the klaxon howled through the boat. The crew of the *Nautilus* manned their diving stations, and the vessel submerged rapidly: 100 . . . 200 . . . 300 feet were indicated by the depth meter. The speed changed to *Slowly Ahead*. Cautiously the nuclear submarine thrust its way under the ice on a northerly course. No one knew yet how thick the Arctic icecap actually was, whether the deep "roots" of ice floes might not suddenly crack the boat. "It was uncanny," Lieutenant Steven A. White said afterward. "True,

we couldn't see the ice, but we all felt as if we were in a coffin
with the lid being closed very slowly."

Besides officers and members of the crew, Dr. Waldo K.
Lyon and his assistant were on board. They were indeed successful in obtaining more information about the Arctic in the
first few hours than other explorers previously had gathered in
years. According to Commander Anderson it was also found
that much of the data published by the Russians about the
Arctic Ocean was, for some reason, inaccurate.

Before the boat's departure from San Diego, Dr. Lyon had
had extra sonar equipment provided for the *Nautilus* to sound
the bottom, surface and anything floating or swimming in
between. Thus the sailors were able to see the covering of ice
above them in the form of lines on graphs, which a special
instrument drew on an unwinding coil of paper. These lines
showed, for example, that the Arctic icecap was a huge moving
mass floating above them. In many places, it was cracked, thin
and crumbling, so that a surface ship could easily get through.
The greater part, however, consisted of loose ice floes, some
only a few yards, others hundreds or even thousands of yards
long.

Using sonars, Dr. Lyon was able to establish two important
facts after the first few hours: The ice of the Arctic Ocean
has by no means been worn smooth underneath by the sea
water, as had been supposed, but is like a crater landscape full
of knolls and hollows. And the "glass" lid over the Pole is considerably thinner that it was believed to be; it is at the average
a little more than ten feet thick.

After the boat had been crawling along for an hour, Commander Anderson gave orders to surface slowly and carefully.
Tensely he watched the reaction of the sonars. At that moment, they were the only means of telling how deep the boat
was beneath the expanse of ice. When the *Nautilus* came to
rest fifteen feet below the ice, Anderson carefully sent up the

periscope. He beheld a dead, phantom world. The pale sunlight just penetrated the ice, giving the water a ghostly color. Loose floes drifted above like large gray clouds. Later he said: "It was quite a fascinating sight which gave me goose pimples and made me feel quite nervous; so I had the periscope hauled in again and told the inquisitive crew rather to watch the ice on the reel of paper."

Mile after mile the *Nautilus* crawled on, the scientific instruments gathering valuable information, the sonar measuring the thickness of the ice and the depth below, which varied between six and ten thousand feet; thermometers indicated the temperature of the sea water, salinity was measured, and samples of the water were taken and tested for signs of life.

After 112 miles the *Nautilus* decided to return for the rendezvous with the *Trigger*. On her way back, the sonar indicated a large gap in the ice and Commander Anderson decided to surface in order to see the Arctic from above. While the *Nautilus* was rising slowly, a shudder went through the boat. The periscope's field of vision blacked out. It must have been damaged by an ice floe which had surged into the gap and hit the boat. The only thing for them to do was to get back to the edge of the ice and inspect the damage. At 1500 hours sharp, seven hours after the journey under ice, the *Nautilus* surfaced right alongside the *Trigger*.

By eight o'clock the next morning, after the damaged periscope had been repaired, the atomic submarine was ready to start again. Commander Kelly of the *Trigger* was informed not to expect the return of the nuclear submarine for the next two to five days, as the *Nautilus* intended to go as far as the 83rd parallel and even farther if possible.

This time the crew accepted the "shutting of the coffin lid" with calm indifference, feeling themselves in an "aquarium that has not been cleaned out for the last few years." The boat cruised 120 feet below the icecap at a speed of twenty knots, until something totally unforeseen happened: the *Nautilus* lost its way.

The most difficult problem in traveling under the Arctic ice is navigation, not because of the ice but because of the proximity of the Pole, where magnetic compasses cease to function and even a good gyrocompass will not work properly. Beyond 70° North they may simply go haywire. This hazard had, of course, been known long before, and so the *Nautilus* had been equipped with a new, improved Mark 19 gyrocompass for its polar voyage. As the boat crossed the 83rd parallel, the conventional magnetic compass started to spin wildly. At the same time, the standard gyrocompass went on strike. Only the large special compass seemed to work normally, and thus the boat continued to the 84th and 85th parallels. The North Pole was only five degrees further on and thus in their immediate vicinity. Shortly before reaching the 86th parallel, the large gyrocompass also broke down. Its revolutions became irregular and finally slowed down. The navigator, William G. Lalor, soon identified the trouble as a blown fuse, and not, as had been feared, the proximity of the Pole. Thus the failure of an apparently insignificant piece of equipment caused the great *Nautilus* to lose its orientation.

When a gyrocompass is turned off in normal waters, it takes about four hours to stabilize it again. How long it would take so near to the North Pole no one on board could say, for no such event had ever occurred in the history of navigation. Both crew and officers had to wait seven hours for the Mark 19 to settle down, though they continued to cruise as best they could with the aid of their magnetic compass. At the 87th parallel, about 180 miles from the Pole, Commander Anderson ordered a retreat, not wanting to expose either the crew or the ship to the danger of suddenly emerging off the Russian coast or, even worse, getting under the belt of solid ice which joins the mainland, both very conceivable eventualities, as the boat

had no means of orienting itself accurately. During this epi-
sode, Major Keating, the hospital corpsman, couldn't resist
writing several notes which he then sealed in bottles and
ejected through the pneumatic garbage tube. Neatly penned in
Russian, they said: "Help, I'm a prisoner in an American
atomic submarine."

Naturally, the *Nautilus* could have surfaced through one of
the cracks and radioed for help, but Commander Anderson
tried to find the way back alone with the aid of the magnetic
compass. He could only guess the course, for the needle was
swinging anywhere within a 60° arc. However, one and a half
days later the sonars showed that the *Nautilus* was now in ice-
free waters, and the magnetic compass was working perfectly
again. After seventy-four hours under ice, during which time
the nuclear submarine covered a thousand miles, it again surfaced safely beside the *Trigger*.

Thus ended the first part of the project, and once the
NATO autumn maneuvers in the Atlantic were over, the
Nautilus returned to San Diego. During the voyage its instruments had recorded over eleven thousand different readings of
ice and water in the Arctic Ocean, and its echo sounders had
provided an accurate profile of the ice ceiling and the ocean bed
for the stretch covered. Scientists in the laboratories of the Submarine and Arctic Research Division in San Diego immediately
began evaluating this mountain of information, a job which
took them months. It yielded some important revelations about
the Arctic seas and justified their hopes of catching up with the
Russians' lead in this field.

The U.S. Navy recognized that whoever controls the seas
around the North Pole will also be able to control the Northern
Hemisphere: nuclear submarines would be able to surface in the
cracks of the Arctic icecap and cover several targets on the
mainland of Russia with their rockets. On the other hand, a
boat like the *Triton* could extend America's radar warning

system by several hundred miles to the north. On ice floes or ice packs rocket bases, radar stations, warehouses, runways and hangars could be erected by laying prefabricated steel netting over the ice with the aid of helicopters and freezing it over with water. Indeed, Dr. W. D. Kingery of the Massachusetts Institute of Technology has developed an ice "alloy" to be used as building material in the Arctic and Antarctic. As natural ice is rather breakable, he mixed a small quantity of glass fibers with water and allowed this "alloy" to freeze. It was then found to be ten times firmer than before, indeed sufficiently solid to be able to construct runways, housing, submarine shelters and harbors of ice on ice. A bar of the new alloy only one-quarter inch in diameter is so firm that it can bear the weight of a grown man. "We have conquered the ice of the Arctic Ocean," says Dr. Kingery. "Now we are learning to make it serve our purposes and to work with it." The Arctic Ocean will one day certainly be as populated as the coastal areas of other oceans.

In June of 1958, the *Nautilus* once again set out to sea, this time from Pearl Harbor and in complete secrecy. It had found a faithful companion in the nuclear-powered sister ship *Skate*. Each vessel's task was to explore certain regions of the Arctic Ocean "at and in the immediate surroundings of the Pole."

"We must now concentrate our energy on a thorough investigation of the Arctic Ocean," Commander Anderson told his crew shortly after departing. This time the passage to the Pole was to be through the Pacific Ocean and the Bering Strait, a waterway less than sixty-five miles wide separating Alaska and Siberia. This stretch proved a much less accessible entrance to the Arctic Ocean than the one used on the previous trip. Adjacent to the Bering Strait is the Chukchi Sea, which is relatively shallow in places, sometimes only just over one hundred feet. It was here that thick layers of ice impeded the path of the *Nautilus*. Some reached over sixty feet into the water, and the submarine could pass under them only with difficulty, its conning tower but a few feet below the ice. At one point, the sonars indicated an ice barrier that reached eighty feet deep and extended for two miles across the East Siberian Sea. The *Nautilus* came through almost crawling on the ocean floor. As another three hundred miles of shallow, ice-covered water lay ahead before reaching the true Arctic Ocean, it was decided to turn back and make a second attempt when the ice had receded further.

On the first of August, 1958, at 0437 hours the *Nautilus* once again prepared to submerge not far north of Point Barrow in Alaska. This time everything went off without a hitch. As in the previous attempt, a completely new kind of navigational device had been installed, a so-called Inertial Navigator. It is a sign of this new era of three-dimensional shipping that this computer-like mechanism was originally developed by North American Aviation to guide the long-range Navaho missile. It continuously indicates the position of the vessel by "remembering" where it was some moments before.

On Sunday, August 3, 1958, at 2315 hours the *Nautilus* became the first vessel in the world to reach the North Pole. It continued farther under the ice into the Sea of Greenland and surfaced on the fifth of August. Exactly sixty-nine hours had passed since it left Point Barrow in Alaska. One hundred and sixteen men had covered 1,830 miles under ice in the complete security and comfort (by submarine standards) of their quarters, enjoying music, moving pictures and warm showers.

The oceanographers on board had been able to take many new readings under much easier conditions than heretofore, to check old information which earlier explorers like Peary, Nansen and Sverdrup had obtained only after months, even years, of sacrifice and self-denial. The depth of the water at the North Pole was remeasured, and was found to be 13,200 feet. The sub also discovered a deep-sea valley with ridges 300 to 1,200 feet high as well as several underwater mountain ranges previously unknown. On the second of August, at 76° 22′, the depth indicated by the echo soundings suddenly jumped from 11,600 feet to 3,000 feet. The boat had come upon an underwater mountain. It traveled seventy miles over the mountain before the reading dropped to 11,600 feet again.

Nowadays journeys under the polar ice belong to the routine duties of American nuclear submarines. Only a week after the *Nautilus* had opened up the new Northwest Passage, the *Skate* crossed the Arctic icecap on an extensive exploratory voyage. In ten days and fourteen hours it covered 2,045 miles in the polar regions, surfacing nine times between the drifting floes of the pack ice, at times no further than fifteen hundred miles from Moscow and Leningrad and less than five hundred miles from Murmansk. Seven months later the same ship undertook a second voyage under the ice from the Atlantic side. By this time the openings in the ice so common in summer had disappeared, and were frozen up in the cold of winter. Nevertheless, everywhere the *Skate* discovered a thin spot, it broke through the ice, proving by its twelve-day voyage that the Arctic can even be navigated in winter by rocket-carrying submarines. The exact thickness of ice that the *Skate* can penetrate is kept secret for strategic reasons, but it is known that another nuclear submarine with a reinforced conning tower pierced an ice ceiling nearly two feet thick. That was the 2,310-ton *Sargo*, which reached the North Pole on the ninth of February, 1960, after a voyage via the Bering Strait. The boat spent thirty-one days underwater and in the course of its cruise covered approximately six thousand miles.

The voyages of the U.S. nuclear submarines under the Arctic icecap have shrunk our earth a little more. The shortest sea route from Tokyo to London, normally a distance of 10,958 nautical miles, would be only 7,530 miles by the polar route; the standard route from New York to Tokyo at present amounts to 9,638 nautical miles, but would be only 7,512 miles going via Baffin Bay, northern Canada and the Bering Strait. Similarly, the journey from the American West Coast to England and all other North Atlantic ports is shorter by way of the Polar icecap than by traditional shipping routes. On polar routes, ships could cover the distance between Europe and ports on America's West Coast twice as fast as ships on conventional routes. In practical terms, this means that the cargo from continent to continent may be doubled.

7   Fleets of Tomorrow

Designs for the vessels of tomorrow's fleet, the first to use the route opened up by the *Nautilus*, have already come off the drawing boards in great number. This work is carried on in silence, without any of the fanfare usually connected with the launching of every new space rocket. Thanks to the experience gained by the American nuclear submarines, various kinds of underwater tankers are at an advanced stage of development in England, France and Japan.

When Vice-Admiral Bernard L. Austin remarked at the launching of the *Triton* that "some of our more futuristic dreamers have talked of whole fleets that submerge," these visions were already turning into actuality. As early as 1959, the U.S. Maritime Administration had published various recommendations for submarine tankers. The suggested underwater ships would have a maximum displacement of 40,000 tons and a speed of 40 knots. Smaller tankers between 20,000 and 40,000 with speeds between 20 and 40 knots were then under study. While noting the many intricate problems that would have to be solved, the agency insisted that "the potential advantages of a subsurface ship make it desirable for the Maritime Administration to continue to investigate the possibilities of such a ship in order to assure that the American merchant marine does not lag in the application of any scientific advance which might ultimately aid it commercially."

Two American companies, Aerojet General Corporation and General Dynamics Corporation, both active in the realm of space technology, have already built test models of submarine tankers with which to conduct experiments in large inland water basins. Engine rooms and crew accommodations on such tankers are similar in construction and placement to those on submarines, though they are on three decks (as in the *Triton*). The oil cargo surrounds the accommodation area as the white of an egg surrounds the yolk, thus protecting the crew and engine compartment from water pressure. Ballast tanks enable the tanker to surface when loaded.

The Japanese Mitsubishi Company also began testing a model submarine ship in the summer of 1959 outside the port of Kobe. Early in 1960, the same company went further and called for the construction of a nuclear-powered submarine freighter with a displacement of up to 35,000 tons and a speed of 22 knots, for the earliest possible use by the Japanese merchant fleet.

The French engineer Rougeron has likewise designed a nuclear-powered, underwater tanker, to be operated by a so-called hydrojet plant. Water is drawn in by suction at the ship's bow and is expelled at the stern with great pressure. Rougeron's ship is intended to be bigger than the *Queen Elizabeth*, and is designed for a speed of more than 60 mph.

Nor does Britain intend to stick exclusively to surface ships. Their Mitchel Engineering Company has designed an underwater giant of 100,000 tons. It will be more than a thousand feet longer than the *Queen Elizabeth*, able to glide through the Atlantic or round the Cape of Good Hope to the Middle East at fifty to sixty knots per hour. With advances in automation, the crew can be limited to a mere dozen. Trials with a model of such a giant were already under way in 1960. At the same time, a smaller submarine tanker by the same company was designed to have a loading capacity of thirty thousand tons while its gross tonnage would amount to fifty thousand. The vessel, which should cost about $46 million, was nicknamed *Moby Dick*. Designed to cruise under water between Canada and England via the Pole, it could carry cargoes of ore at all seasons of the year.

In 1959, a delegation of British shipbuilders and shipowners went to Canada to examine Diana Bay in the north to see whether ship landings there were possible in winter. With underwater merchant ships, harbors on the northernmost coastlines of all continents will become a necessity. Indeed, the U.S. Atomic Energy Commission has drawn up plans for a harbor beyond the polar circle near Cape Thompson on the northwest coast of Alaska as part of Project Chariot, which aims to create an artificial basin by exploding five H-bombs, or the equivalent of 280,000 tons of TNT. The new harbor will eventually form the most northerly base for American military submarines and future underwater mercantile fleets.

Opponents of these different projects say that the construction of submarine tankers would be from three to ten times as expensive as that of surface tankers. The champions of the cause retort that the new ships would soon justify the extra costs, including those of the construction of new harbors.

a) Quite apart from the fact that underwater merchant ships could travel via the shorter polar route, they would be far less vulnerable in wartime than conventional surface convoys. This assertion has historical backing. During both world wars, German U-boats were able to carry cargo back and forth from besieged Europe to South America. At the end of the Second World War, the Germans had almost completed construction of large underwater vessels which would have had enough range to refuel submarines in almost any ocean of the world.

b) Some pessimists, believing in the impending destruction of mankind, think of the submarine freighters as a new Noah's

Ark. A select group or elite, they say, could survive the most fearful nuclear war by remaining submerged for an indefinite period.

c) To attain a given speed much less energy is expended under water than on the surface. A ship under water does not have to contend with either the wind or the even greater braking effect of its own bow waves. The *Queen Mary* can reach thirty knots at the expense of 150,000 hp. To double that speed she would need engines producing 1.5 million hp and consuming five times more fuel. No such ship would be worth building because engines and diesel fuel alone would use up all available space. An eighty-thousand-ton submarine tanker, on the other hand, could attain a speed of sixty knots at the expense of only one-third the energy demanded by an equally large surface ship.

d) Another factor in favor of submarine merchant ships is that adverse weather conditions could no longer affect them. The *Queen Mary*, with her normal speed of thirty knots, has to slow down to ten or twelve knots in bad winter weather. Nothing of this sort would happen to a submarine, even were a hurricane raging above the water. Just as the *George Washington* counteracts the motion of the sea with a thirty-ton stabilizer, so the tankers would glide through the water with practically no roll or pitch.

e) Eventually man will use regular convoys of submarine barges, towing behind them a chain of enormous, sausage-like containers. The United States Rubber Company and several European firms have already designed rubber containers for surface transportation of various liquid cargoes. Bigger versions, 20 feet in diameter and 360 feet long, would be ideal for high-seas traffic. Every "rubber sausage" of this size could hold 182,000 gallons of freight and several of them could be towed by a single submarine tanker. Admiral Momsen is convinced that by 1980 such submarine barge trains will be almost a mile long, transporting some seventy-five different liquids ranging from oil, petrol, alcohol and acids to fine-grained materials like cement or grain. One great advantage would be that no reloading would be necessary if the purchaser was located inland. Tugs could continue to convey the goods by river to the point nearest the final destination.

One needs but little imagination to form a picture of the development of tomorrow's fleets, what their vessels might look like and how they will navigate. For instance, a submarine, at present, is most likely to be detected when it surfaces to take its bearings from the stars, as seamen have done for centuries. Naval experts the world over realized years ago that this procedure would have to be avoided. Precision gyrocompasses were one answer, but even they had to be adjusted at regular intervals to avoid a deviation from the prescribed course. These adjustments were made by taking bearings from radio beacons, coastal lights and fixed stars, and this involved surfacing, even if for only a few minutes. Many modern U.S. submarines were equipped with periscopes and computing instruments which could take all these bearings in a matter of seconds. The boats stayed almostly completely submerged, but the periscope could still be detected by an enemy radar. This fact, and the desire for frequent submarine voyages under the polar ice pack, made it mandatory for modern nuclear submarines to navigate accurately while totally submerged for long periods of time. The impossible was finally achieved in 1959, when North American Aviation Company electronics engineers adapted the inertial navigator of the Navaho missile to the *Nautilus* and other nuclear submarines. It guides the boats through the three-dimensional realm of the ocean with an accuracy that approaches the miraculous.

A very simplified explanation might be that the new SINS device (Ship Inertial Navigation System) consists of three gyros each spinning on a different axis at twelve thousand revolutions per minute. The gyros help to hold a so-called "stabilized platform" in a continuous horizontal position, no matter how much the boat is tossed or turned in the water. The platform, like a gyrocompass, only much more precise, accurately indicates the directional quarters at all times, even in the vicinity of the magnetic pole.

Linked with SINS are devices continuously gathering information on the boat's speed, course and other factors relative to its position. One of these instruments, for instance, called JOGLOG, is fixed on the stern and is used to determine the strength and speed of ocean currents crossing the boat's route. All readings made by JOGLOG and the other instruments are continuously fed into NAVDAC, an electronic computer. Previous to a journey, NAVDAC has been fed all pertinent data on the precise point of departure. By comparing this information with all the new data supplied to it by the various instruments during a cruise, NAVDAC can indicate the approximate position of the boat in the ocean at any given moment. Automation has been developed a step further in the case of America's missile-carrying submarines, where NAVDAC's findings are relayed to a battery of sixteen other computers, one for each Polaris. In its electronic brain each computer contains all data on the target for which its missile has been designated. By comparing these data with the information received by NAVDAC it continuously takes care of the necessary adjustments within the guidance and control system of a Polaris. No matter what deviation the boat makes from an originally intended course, each Polaris missile will reach its target with deadly accuracy.

The great advantage of the SINS device is that it is completely unaffected by the weather. Should a storm drive the submarine from its prescribed course the captain can still find his bearings at any time, independently of the outside world. The gyros need no readjustment over fairly lengthy periods, and the readings of NAVDAC are so exact that Commander Anderson of the *Nautilus* once reported: "After seventy hours under the ice I had a better idea of where I was than after a couple of minutes' car ride in London traffic."

The fifty-ton SINS navigation equipment today enables many American submarines correctly to determine their position in the ocean to within a half-mile. With the aid of future navigation satellites, the submarines and ships of the U.S. Navy will soon be able to establish their exact position in the Pacific or Atlantic to one-tenth of a mile.

Transit IB, which went into orbit on the eighteenth of April, 1960, is the first of these "celestial radio beacons," which will cause a revolution in the ancient art of navigation. By 1964 four similar satellites should be launched into parallel orbits. Ships of all nations will be able to pick up the radio signals these satellites emit and thereby determine their position at any time, day or night, in any weather.

One of the very next steps in navigation will probably be the improvement of the SINS equipment to the point where no submarine will ever have to surface to correct its course. It will check NAVDAC's information with the aid of sonar depth readings. For this purpose, however, the entire ocean floor will first have to be surveyed accurately. These eventual maps will show all the floor's unalterable features as well as the intensity of the earth's magnetic field and the force of gravity at every point in the ocean. This is the kind of information invaluable to military submarines, which, as we have already seen, Soviet oceanographers and submarine commanders are keenly collecting at present.

Underwater merchant ships probably would not need the precise, expensive SINS equipment. It seems likely that they will eventually be directed by submarine buoys marking waterways under the surface, with the traffic stacked in layers, as in the case of air transport today. Plastic containers, holding tiny nuclear generators which function for several years, will be anchored at regular intervals under water and with the use of hydrophones, submarine tankers will then only have to tune into the sound waves emitted by these individual buoys. This system might lead to the automatic navigation of ships, where the vessel would be virtually handed from buoy to buoy.

Captains of future submarine freighters will even be able to receive their owners' instructions under water by means of a communications method which was, for a long time, believed impossible to achieve. Since the invention of radio, i.e., during the last sixty years, mountains and valleys have proved to be no obstacle for radio waves. Radio links have been established between continents and even with heavenly bodies. Yet, it seemed utterly impossible to construct a transmitter that could send radio waves from the mainland to below the surface of the ocean, as salt water tends to absorb radio waves of normal length. Only very low-frequency radio waves can penetrate the ocean's surface, and their generation requires enormous power. The Germans, as early as 1939, perfected just such a high-powered transmitting station. Whereas Allied submarines during World War II had to surface or poke their aerials out of the water in order to receive instructions from headquarters (thus incurring the danger of detection), German U-boats could throughout the war receive their orders under water.

Their scientists had erected the mammoth transmitting station, appropriately dubbed Goliath, near the town of Magdeburg. On a wavelength of more than seventeen miles, radio messages were beamed out at certain hours of the day to all German U-boats at sea. Surfacing—or diving—to the so-called *"Programmtiefe"* (program depth) of thirty-six to forty-two feet, they could receive their orders without danger of detection.

Goliath was dismantled after the war and brought to Britain, but the U.S. Navy also eventually benefited from this invention. By 1960 it had completed a long-wave transmitting station similar to Goliath on the Atlantic coast in Maryland, with two antennae as tall as the Eiffel Tower, and twelve smaller antennae. The whole station has a transmitting power of two million watts, forty times as great as the most powerful commercial radio station on earth. First trials were begun in January, 1961, by transmitting orders on wavelengths of one mile to U.S. submarines a hundred feet below the surface of the Atlantic, the Pacific and even the Arctic Ocean.

Dr. Glauco Partel, founder of an Italian rocket company, is convinced that by 1970 all submarines will not only receive underwater messages but will, in turn, be able to communicate with one another under water at great distances and contact headquarters whenever necessary. This, he says, will bring the day even closer when a submarine will remain completely submerged for sustained periods. Like the men of Captain Nemo's *Nautilus*, its crew will derive all oxygen, fresh water, food and perhaps even fuel directly from the ocean.

The first steps in this direction are already being taken. One of the most recent advances in underwater communications, for instance, was announced by the Bendix Corporation in August, 1961. It concerned the development of a system that combines telemetry with sonar to provide cableless underwater communications. "The system, believed to be the first of its kind in the world," represents "the most significant step in underwater electronics since the development of sonar. It will open the doors to new forms of underwater research both by human divers and by instruments," the company announcement said. The new system may well be used one day for communications between submerged submarines, if its present underwater transmitting range of five miles can be substantially increased.

Advances are also constantly being made in the improvement of environmental conditions within a submarine. Besides air-purifying equipment, the first nuclear submarines still had to carry special tanks on their cruises from which shots of oxygen were injected into the boat's atmosphere at regular intervals to keep conditions favorable. The *George Washington* was the first nuclear sub to be equipped with its own oxygen-producing plant. The oxygen was obtained by a process of electrolysis from fresh water which in turn is distilled from sea water. Certain precautions still have to be taken, however, so that the precious air is not contaminated. For instance, the cook must not use animal fat, as it releases eye-irritating enzymes; only vegetable fat may be used. The boat's doctor must be extremely careful with his thermometers, for if they should break, mercury vapor would soon poison the atmosphere. For the same reason no toothpaste or shaving cream may be taken from Aerosol cans as the freon gas that is used in the cans would escape into the submarine's atmosphere. Bleach may not be used in the laundry because of its caustic vapor.

To improve the atmosphere in submarines, it is planned to include seaweed gardens on tomorrow's boats. The algae would not only recondition the stale air by giving off oxygen, but, thanks to their incredible rate of reproduction, also serve as food for the crew. Experiments in this direction are being carried out under the former German U-boat expert, Dr. Karl-Ernst Schäfer, in the laboratories of the Electric Boat Division of the General Dynamics Corporation in Groton, Connecticut.

Thus, future nuclear submarines' length of stay under water will depend solely on the psychic endurance of their crews, and not, as previously, on the supplies of food, fuel and oxygen.

One is inclined to suppose that the more the devices developed for our submarines, the bigger they must become. The *George Washington*'s stabilizer and SINS equipment alone weigh one hundred tons, for example. Larger boats could of course be built, but this would be impracticable because of the cost and crew needed. Therefore, further automation in the form of robots will not only help to save manpower and thus reduce the number of necessary accommodations on a ship, but also increase performance reliability by eliminating the human-error factor. In this field remarkable progress has been made in recent years. One ingenious automatic device is the SUBIC (Submarine Integrated Control) system, an electronic brain no larger than a briefcase. Designed for a new class of nuclear attack submarines, it will automatically gather information from other shipboard instruments, check it and compare it by making fifteen thousand different calculations each second. It then passes the relevant material, such as bearings of boat and target as well as the position of the enemy and information about its own missiles and torpedoes, to the skipper, suggesting on an illuminated screen the best way to attack or escape.

SUBIC will be able to reduce the size of nuclear submarine crews from a hundred to twelve, thus making it possible in the future to build smaller, rather than larger, attack boats, without sacrificing any of the advanced, though sometimes cumbersome electronic equipment contained in some of today's larger submarines. The Navy is already studying the possibility for SUBIC-equipped midget "submarine killers." In a project headed by Richard B. Laning, former commander of the *Seawolf*, it is estimated that the first of these boats, of about one-eighth the size and cost of today's nuclear submarines (at present priced between six to ten million dollars each), should be ready in 1967. Each will carry a crew of only twelve men.

If adaptable to surface ships, a system similar to SUBIC could not only increase the available cargo space by reducing the number of necessary crew accommodations, but also save on crew wages. To ascertain the feasibility of such a system was the purpose of a study conducted early in 1960 by the Maritime Administration. Comparing the crew and wage problem of a ship with that of modern transatlantic jet planes, John J. Allen, Jr., Under Secretary of Commerce for Transportation, said that "these costly big planes, through modern technology, are manned by a handful of people, probably three in the cockpit and three in the cabin. In ships, practically nothing has been done, technologically speaking, to reduce the cost of operation by adapting modern developments."

A later study (*Some Aspects of Automation for Ships*), prepared by R. E. Stillwagon of Westinghouse for the Maritime Research Advisory Committee, showed that on partially automated merchant ships savings in operating, including crew wages, would amount to $5.7 million over a period of twenty years, the normal life expectancy of a ship. Areas where machines could help reduce a ship's operating cost would be the bridge, the engine room and the various cargo-handling sections. In the engine room, for instance, computers would accomplish the major part of control and supervision work. Fed with a detailed work program prior to the voyage, they would also regulate operating routines at sea.

In January of 1962, the world's first partially automated freighter arrived in New York harbor. It was the Japanese 9,800-ton vessel *Kinkasan Maru*, which, according to her captain, Nobu Takebayashi, "is as simple [to steer] as driving an automobile."

Heart of the automatic system is a console no bigger than an office desk, equipped with various knobs for steering, engine speed, etc., etc. It is linked to an air-conditioned control room near the bridge, where a technician watches various dials, lights and needles, each one indicating the functioning of certain parts of machinery aboard the ship.

On her first runs the *Kinkasan Maru* sailed with forty-three men instead of with the normal complement of fifty. Reductions to about thirty men are expected once the automated control system proves itself. Eventually, the Mitsui Line (owner of the automated freighter) will install similar systems on board all its thirty-six ships, which will amount to considerable savings in crew wages.

In order to battle rising operational costs, the U.S. Navy is also hopefully viewing extensive automation of its vessels. In a project called Dyna, a group of officers in the Office of Naval Research is designing a series of ships based on the most advanced technology. The group believes that the crew of technologically advanced nuclear destroyers can be reduced from a complement of 265 officers and men to thirty to sixty men. But even were conventional steam plants to be used in the future, automation could help to reduce propulsion personnel to a half-dozen or less, compared with the fifty or sixty men now needed to serve a ship's power plant. The dollar savings through ship automation on a fleet-wide basis would be impressive: the elimination of an officer could save the Navy, over a twenty-year period, approximately $212,000, and elimination of an enlisted man, $122,000.

Partial automation of Navy surface ships—at first possibly destroyers—may not come before 1970–75, and total automation of merchant ships perhaps not before the end of this century. But we can soon expect partially automated midget submarines.

The debut of the small, fast SUBIC boats will mark the convergence of two until now separate lines of development in ship design. We have seen how the *Trieste* may be considered a sort of "Model T" for future submarines, using its enormous depth capacity to investigate potential operation strategy in all marine regions, while the *Aluminaut* already possesses the maneuverability lacking in the *Trieste*. Experiences gained with these two vessels and the future SUBIC boats will give us the deep-sea midget submarine of the future, a sufficient number of which would provide not only an essential weapon but also a valuable aid in opening up the sea. Such boats are being seriously talked about in Navy circles. With a crew of fifteen and a speed of up to forty knots the first ones will be capable of reaching a depth of five thousand feet. Other, improved versions will operate at even greater depths. "We shall be developing submarines in the future," said Senator Magnuson in 1960, "which will go from ten to twenty thousand feet below the surface of the oceans, into the deep, dark recesses of the oceans. . . . They will go silently, like animals in a jungle." And, according to Dr. Edward Wenk, Jr., one of the nation's leading authorities on submarine design, it now appears feasible to build submarines that could "successfully operate at depths of one, two and even three miles without trade-off sacrifices in speed or combat potency." (Incidentally, Dr. Wenk, now on the staff of President Kennedy's scientific advisers, also helped in the design of the *Aluminaut*.)

In the face of all this it is not too fantastic to imagine fleets of midget submarines undertaking the most diverse tasks anywhere and at all depths in the seas. Dr. Partel has predicted that some of these boats will be ideally suited for antitorpedo torpedoes. When a torpedo is fired with the intention of destroying an enemy vessel, and the latter fires a countertorpedo in return, a smaller torpedo is released from the first one, to hurry on ahead and annihilate the oncoming countertorpedo.

In the more distant future, we can assume that midget submarines would have not a land base but rather a parent ship, itself a submarine. Although designed as an armament depot, the latter could also serve as a large underwater laboratory with big observation windows and all oceanographic exploration apparatus, which for lack of space could not be accommodated on board the midget submarines. These will carry out various tasks or investigations on the ocean floor and then return through sluice chambers into special docks built into the sides of the parent ship. Once the midget subs have entered, the chambers will be closed and pumped dry, so that the crew can unload their haul of specimens. After a rest several thousand feet under the water they will set out on another tour.

None of this is mere speculation. There can be no doubt that even aircraft carriers will one day have to go under water in order to survive nuclear attack. Raymond Blackman, editor of *Jane's Fighting Ships*, in an interview with the magazine *Newsweek* expressed the opinion in 1961 that the forerunners of the underwater carrier of tomorrow are such U.S. nuclear-missile submarines as the *Halibut* with its Regulus missile in a special launching pad forward of the conning tower, and the 425-foot-long submarines of the *Lafayette* class. This prediction comes as less of a surprise if one knows that as early as World War II the *Deutsche Kriegsmarine* had operational submarines that were equipped with midget airplanes. Launched by catapult, the plane could stay on the lookout and spy for enemy targets of pursuing destroyers long before they came into visual range of the submarine itself.

The construction of submersible aircraft carriers as well as submarines for the greatest depths will benefit immensely from the vast strides made in recent years in the field of metallurgy. Steel and aluminum alloys of the greatest strength have been developed for space vehicles, as well as new processing techniques of refractory metals such as titanium and beryllium. On a submarine a thin hull of titanium or beryllium is the equivalent of a thick hull of steel or aluminum. Titanium submarines, for instance, would be able to dive ten to fifteen times as deep as the *Nautilus* without impairing their maneuverability. Thanks to these new building materials and techniques some experts are even thinking of permanently manned stations on the ocean floor.

Tomorrow's submerged navies will also bring with them an increasing number of underwater harbors and military installations on the ocean floor. For strategic reasons the Swedes have already blasted their rocky coastline to provide accommodation for their destroyers. The same could be done for submarines, with access tunnels below the coastal water line. Admiral Momsen, in an article called "The Coming Death of Our Surface Navy," suggested blowing underwater tunnels into the rocky California coast. A submarine ship could enter such a tunnel, a gate would close behind it and, as in a lock, part of the water inside the tunnel would then be pumped out. A second gate would then open and the boat could enter an underwater harbor. Elevators would give access to the earth's surface three to five hundred feet above. Other marine experts such as Dr. Partel believe that one day we will have not only underwater harbors but also streets and even cities on the ocean floor.

Some of these underwater installations may become reality within a few years. The Firestone Tire & Rubber Co., for instance, is testing a 10,000-gallon underwater fuel-storage system in the Gulf of Mexico. It consists of saucer-shaped nylon bags which could store not only fuel but food and other supplies as well. Proposed is a military storage depot, anchored far out at sea. If a submarine were short in supplies, it would be directed to one of these depots. Then several of its crew members, in diver's suits, would make the necessary connections under water to take food or fuel aboard.

Dr. Partel also has some interesting theories about the future development of ship propulsion. He believes that submarine boats will soon be driven on rocket and jet propulsion principles. Also, according to him, exhaustive biological and oceanographic studies in the future may open up a way of using sea water itself as fuel, at least in surface ships. "A photoelectric cell can be envisaged," he said in 1959, "which will reduce water to hydrogen and oxygen, gases which burn together. . . . This process could be continued as long as a sunlight source was available." Of course, enough oxygen and hydrogen could be produced and stored while above water for use in underwater cruises. Another possible fuel for underwater vessels, Partel believes, may be the use of plankton, readily available in many ocean areas.

Late in 1961 it became known that the U.S. Navy is indeed experimenting with a new kind of battery that uses sea matter as fuel to provide the flow of electricity. Details of this so-called "bio-battery" are classified. It was merely announced that the power levels achieved so far were high enough to operate radio beacons, signal lights and other small, navigational aids.

Eventually, bio-batteries will be used to power a new class of submarines and, if efficient methods could be devised to obtain enough fuel from the sea, whole cities could be provided with electricity from the ocean.

One of the ways of increasing the speed of surface ships will be to change the kind of propellers used. A new invention, the so-called supercavitation propeller, which is already being tested on ship models in England and America, should enable submarine tankers to travel at 125 mph or more. Conventionally shaped ships' propellers work in a push-and-pull manner, and have one major disadvantage: As their revolutions increase, hundreds of little vapor bubbles form on the forward side of their blades. Though they burst almost immediately, new bubbles are constantly created. This process, called cavitation, causes a bombardment of the propeller blades with highly undesirable vibrations which tends to damage the screw. For instance, it has been observed that cavitation can produce fist-size holes in the bronze propeller of a large ocean liner after only two or three voyages. But the damage caused by cavitation is less significant than the braking effect created by the constantly imploding bubbles, which considerably diminishes a screw's pulling power, thus leaving the propulsion mainly to its pushing power. The new supercavitation propeller, thanks to its different shape (see illustration 14), eliminates the braking effect of the bubbles to a great extent. It is, however, very noisy and therefore unsuitable for submarines, though it will definitely be applied to underwater freighters, surface ships and very likely to a new revolutionary type of craft called the hydrofoil.

The hydrofoil concept has led to the design of ships able to cross the oceans at speeds of 100 to 200 mph. These ships will ride on foils, similar in form and structure to airplane wings. As soon as a hydrofoil ship reaches, say, 25 mph, it rises out of the waves and speeds along on these foils. Thus, resistance of the water and bow wash is reduced to a minimum, for the latter only slightly affects the relatively thin and streamlined foils.

Some of the first hydrofoil boats were developed in Germany. They consisted of relatively small, fast craft for amphibious landings. Larger boats of this type were perfected after the war and today run as passenger ferries on European lakes, rivers and coastal waters such as the lakes of Zurich and Constance, the Elbe River and the straits separating Italy from Sicily. The Russians have for over a year operated a hydrofoil on the Black Sea. Their latest boat of this type is a ferry called *Sputnik* with a capacity of three hundred passengers. Launched in 1961, it attains a speed of 50 mph and is said to be the world's largest hydrofoil.

Unfortunately, in the United States and Canada hydrofoils were built for many years solely on an experimental basis. At last, in 1959 the Maritime Administration decided to give the idea a practical try and ordered an eighty-ton boat to be built by the Grumman Aircraft Company. Launched in the summer of 1961, the *Denison* can carry seventy to eighty passengers at a speed of close to seventy mph. Other companies, such

as North American Aviation and Boeing Airplane, are also
getting into the design of hydrofoils. In the summer of 1961
the latter company was awarded a contract by the Navy's
Bureau of Ships for the construction of a three-man fifteen-
ton, twin-hull hydrofoil.

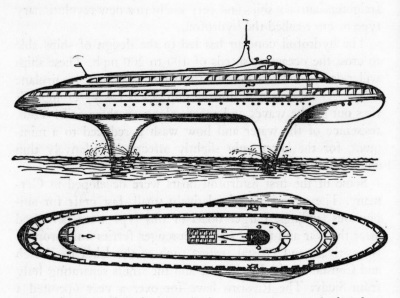

Design of a "hydrofoil" for transatlantic voyages. At a speed of 12 knots
the boat's hull will rise out of the water. As the swell loses its effect on the
ship, the vessel can reach a speed of 60 mph.

While U.S. hydrofoils are still fairly small, the West German engineer Herman Wendel has completed plans for transatlantic hydrofoils capable of transporting several hundred
passengers from Hamburg to New York in barely two days.
Eventually such ships will be nuclear-powered and will cross
from continent to continent at speeds of up to 125 mph.

Thus one of the prospects in this age of naval revolution is that one day all ships will very likely sail either over or under the water instead of directly on the surface as they have done for centuries. Lately there has been much talk of vessels that can travel on a cushion of slightly compressed air. Called "ground-effect" vehicles, they are propelled by a principle as remarkable as it is simple. Engines draw in air and eject it again through a series of vents on the flat underside of the "ship." The cushion of air that is formed forces the vessel out of the water. It will rise inches or even feet above the waves, depending on the force of the ejected air. Additional streams of air are ejected from the stern, to push the vehicle forward. These streams can be channeled through ducts at the sides of the vehicle to move it in any desired horizontal direction.

A number of boats whose operation is based on the "ground effect" are already in advanced stages of design or construction in England. The famous flying-boat company, Saunders-Roe, built the so-called hovercraft, which, as the name indicates, can hover equally well above land or water. It hovered across the British Channel in 1959. The same company started designing a larger version of this craft early in 1960 and hopes to complete a ground-effect passenger ferry in a few years.

In spite of the problems still to be overcome, many inventors hail the development of ground-effect vehicles as immensely important in the travel of the future, for they can travel equally well over land *and* sea, thus representing a peculiar combination of ship, airplane and automobile. Hovercrafts may one day entirely transform our whole concept of what a transport system can be. Bridges would become unnecessary, since ground-effect vehicles can "land" just as well on dry land as on water. Some of the world's great ports would lose their monopoly of the traffic now assured by their geographical location. Instead of berthing at a pier, a hovercraft could, if necessary, continue right inland. Frozen meat from

Chicago, for example, would no longer have to be brought to New York by rail to be loaded onto ships for exporting. A hovercraft could instead be loaded directly in the yard of a slaughterhouse and then take the shortest land-sea route to its ultimate destination.

In the United States, Bell Aerosystem is building a so-called "Hydroskimmer" for the Navy. Based on a principle similar to a hovercraft, the 62-foot-long vessel will be able to carry five tons of freight at 70 knots per hour over land and sea.

Looking ahead to the year 2000 one can even envision private transatlantic journeys by hovercraft. Several such vessels, each with a diameter of one mile, could float in the Atlantic, 250 miles apart. They would include parking places, filling stations, repair workshops and hotels. Tourists would then hop from one hovercraft island to the next in family-sized ground-effect vehicles of their own (already being designed by Curtiss-Wright). They could cross the Atlantic in a couple of days and then continue their journey overland.

Ships of a mile in diameter would, in fact, be artificial islands, one of the necessary requisites for a practical development of the sea. In theory there are no objections to such a size; the vast surface area of the oceans offers enough space. Inhabitants of such gigantic "floating" cities would draw their food from the sea, not by simply getting what came their way, but rather by cultivating the oceans in the same manner as agriculture is today practiced on land.

Other experts dare predict that man himself will develop a form of life on and in the oceans of the world. "Man will probably be able to make free dives to a depth of three thousand feet," the Swiss scientist-adventurer, Hannes Keller, told specialists of the U.S. Navy in 1960. He is the first man to have dived deeper than 510 feet (a good skin-diver can dive two hundred feet) protected by nothing more than a rubber suit and a self-contained breathing apparatus (commonly called an

Aqualung). Keller achieved this remarkable feat by inhaling special gases prior to his dive, a technique that is his own discovery. In a pressure-tank test Keller was subjected to a pressure equal to a depth of 820 feet, without suffering any ill effects. If Keller's technique can be used by other divers it will mean that all the continental shelves down to a depth of 820 feet or more could be explored by skin-diving oceanographers. The combined area of regions at this depth is said to be twice the size of Europe.

Dr. Glauco Partel even goes one step further in predicting the adaptability of man to life under water, by saying that "our frogmen will one day have artificial gills at their disposal." This is also the conviction of Jacques-Yves Cousteau, who told various American scientists in 1960: "In years to come people will be able to 'breathe' under water by means of artificial gills which will be planted into their body in a minor surgical operation and removed in the same manner. One day everything that is commonplace on land will be possible in the sea as well. This will mean the conquest of a new planet. The sea will indeed become a second earth."

Russia's Professor G. V. Petrovich shares this opinion. Rather than setting up large cities on other planets (should the need arise to resettle part of the world's growing population) Petrovich is looking to the oceans of our earth for a more economical solution. It would be cheaper to build cities on and below the Seven Seas, he says, than to build cities on satellites in space.

"Life began in the sea, and it is certain that man will now return more and more to the ocean!"

8　The Population Explosion

Petrovich's idea of building submarine "relief" towns for the increasing world population may sound fantastic, but it is not without parallel. Lieutenant Commander George F. Bond of the U.S. Navy made a similar proposal for "extensive underwater suburbs" which would include all the facilities of a modern community. All structures for his submarine town could be prefabricated on land before being sunk in the sea near the coast. Powerful floodlights would illuminate the roads for the inhabitants commuting in divers' outfits and midget submarines. Nuclear reactors would supply the current for the submarine town, and air could be pumped through large pipe lines from the mainland should the oxygen obtained from the sea itself become insufficient.

In his underwater towns, Bond not only sees a suitable protection from the effects of atomic war, but he believes them to offer the best accommodation for the crowds being forced off the land by the growing world population.

"The sea is the cheapest alternative for our overpopulated earth. It is less expensive erecting suburbs on the sea bed than settling emigrants on other planets, and one day it will probably be necessary." Certainly this plan is fantastic and it will be realized only in the distant future, if at all. Why, then, shall we hear many more such proposals in coming years and decades? Bond gave the answer in an interview: "In a few hundred years there simply will not be room for man's ever-increasing numbers, and agricultural lands will be too precious to erect new towns or factories on them."

Such a lack of space is already being felt in Japan, for example, where serious consideration is being given to making the sea habitable. Where today fishing craft still sail over the Bay of Tokyo, by the end of the century there will be a gigantic concrete cylinder housing a new suburb protected from the sea. Tokyo's town planners intend to let hundreds of concrete tubes down into the water and then join them together to make one large dam wall with a circumference of twenty miles. It will be situated two to five miles from the coast, where the bed is flat rock. Then the water will be pumped out of this mighty basin and streets, estates and factories will be built on what was once the sea floor. Thirty to fifty feet above the streets, on the outside of the eighty-foot-high concrete wall, the port of this odd city will be constructed. Tunnels under the sea will maintain traffic communications with other suburbs of Japan's metropolis, and this new borough of the city will draw its power from natural gas resources in the Bay of Tokyo. With this original plan, Tokyo's city council hopes to find essential space for the millions of new citizens who will be settling in the capital in the future. The city already numbers over nine million or one-tenth of Japan's total population.

Admittedly the building of dikes is nothing new in man's endeavor to win land back from the sea; the Dutch have been practicing it for decades, chiefly to extend their farmland. The Tokyo dam-building project, however, is the first in history aimed at relieving the congestion in living space.

The world population has grown so rapidly in the last ten years that people have begun talking about the P-bomb ("Population bomb") in anxious terms, as well as of a "population explosion." Every year, a United Nations report reads, the world's population increases by forty-five to fifty million people, the equivalent to the total population of France. Every minute eighty-five children are being born into the world. The table below shows impressively the rate at which the world population is increasing:

Year	World Population (in millions)
1800	906 (estimated)
1850	1,171 "
1900	1,608 "
1950	2,476 "
1955	2,691 "
1959	2,800 "
1960	2,900 "
1975	3,828 "
1980	4,200 "
2000	6,267–6,900 "

The chief reasons for this disquieting increase in the population lies in the fact that the hard-won knowledge of modern medicine and hygiene has brought about an enormous decline in the mortality rates of every land, in South America, for instance, by as much as 50 percent. Nowadays there isn't a single country where the infant mortality rate hasn't improved over the past fifty years, while adults' life expectancy has been raised immensely.

"If the present birth rate is maintained and the death rate remains so low, theoretically the population one thousand years from now will only have room to stand," declared Dr. L. Matthews, director of the London Zoological Society, in September, 1959. "Certainly nature will see to a reduction in the human race, as soon as this point is reached. Part will starve, or devastating plagues or an atomic war will solve the problem."

Professor Hans Freudenberg, medical statistician at the Free

1.—Professor Auguste Piccard's submersible *Trieste*, being lowered to the water. Notice the crew compartment under the float. (U.S. Navy)

2.—Professor Piccard with his son in a model of the diving bell at the German Industrial Fair, Hanover, 1960. (Ullstein—dpa)

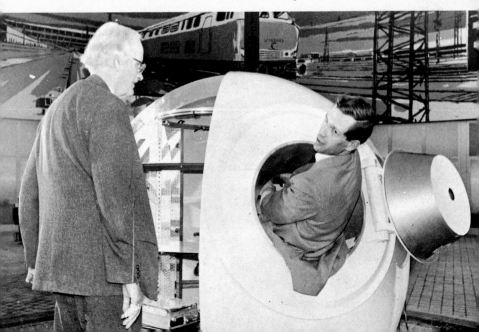

3.—"At 20,000 feet the sea floor looks like the Sahara," Don Walsh and Jacques Piccard said about this photo. (U.S. Navy)

4.—Drawing shows the world's deepest diving submarine. Designed to travel at depths of 15,000 feet, the 50-foot-long American *Aluminaut* will become operational in 1962 or 1963. (Reynolds Metals Company)

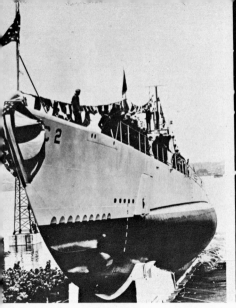

5. (a)—Revolution in submarine building. The boat on the left, built twenty-five years ago, retains the shape of a surface ship.

    (b)—The atomic submarine *Skipjack* (right) was constructed on completely new principles. Its whale-like hull enables it to attain much higher speeds. (General Dynamics Corporation)

6.—The *Skipjack* on exercises in the Long Island Sound. (U.S. Navy)

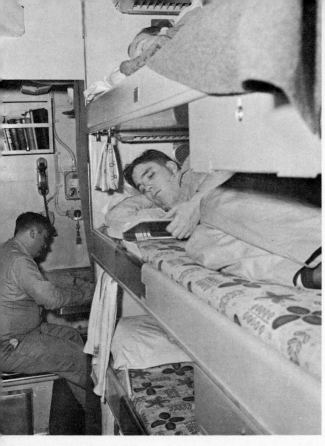

7. & 8.—More space in nuclear submarines gives the crew greater comfort than conventional submarines could offer. Every bunk has its own heating, while the mess serves a variety of courses on white china. (U.S. Navy)

9.—Polar expeditions without strain—an American nuclear submarine on a voyage through the Arctic Ocean. The *Skate* submerges amid the ice, and two members of the crew stretch their legs doing a bit of reconnaissance. (U.S. Navy)

10.—Below, the crew of the *Sargo* hoisting the flag of the American state Hawaii at the North Pole. Notice the rope ladder hanging from the conning tower in the background. (U.S. Navy)

11.—The *Nautilus*, the American atomic submarine, which was the first to open up a new shipping route via the North Pole icecap, when it covered the distance under the ice in ninety-six hours. (Keystone)

12.—The spacious mess hall in this modern submarine. (U.S. Navy)

13.—One of the old variety of ship's screws now shown to be so uneconomical. (U.S. Navy)

14.—Contrast the above screw with this new super-cavitation propeller, the effect of which is said to raise the speed of many ships at least five-fold. (U.S. Navy)

15.—Hidden within a column of compressed air and water, a Polaris missile rises from the American submarine *George Washington* during a test firing. (U.S. Navy)

16.—The *George Washington* on one of its voyages. (Ullstein—dpa)

17. (a)—A hovercraft on the Thames in front of the Houses of Parliament. The boat ejects compressed air downward, forcing itself up and riding on a cushion of air. As all friction and resistance from the water are eliminated it is possible for such a vehicle to attain an incredible speed of 50 knots. (dpa)

(b)—Hydrofoil craft could cross the Atlantic in less than three days. Here is an artist's concept of a passenger-carrying vessel. Its submerged foils act like the wings of an airplane to lift the hull out of the water, enabling the craft to skim smoothly over the surface. (General Electric Company)

18.—While the U.S. Maritime Administration is still engaged with feasibility studies of large hydrofoil craft, *Sputnik*, a Russian vessel of this type, is already in active service. It has accommodation for 300 passengers and a maximum speed of 50 miles an hour. (Wide World)

19.—A Swiss hovercraft on the Lake of Zurich, where it reached a speed of over 40 m.p.h. (Keystone)

20.—America's dream is already a reality in Russia: submarines specially for ocean research. Here, an observer at one of the windows converses with the leader of the expedition on board the *Severjanka*. (TASS)

21.—This is the vessel that Jacques-Yves Cousteau has designed for observing marine life. It takes a crew of two, who, lying on their stomachs, can look through the two "eyes." The small window in between is for filming.(© 1959 National Geographic Society. Photograph by Thomas J. Abercrombie.)

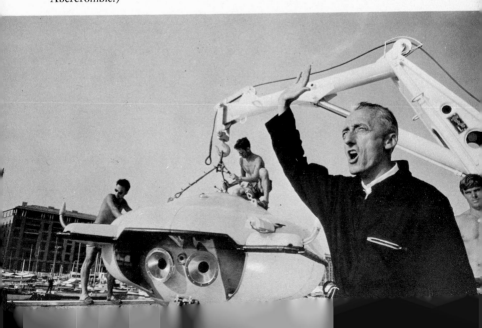

22.—This odd-looking contraption, called RUM, is a remote-controlled underwater manipulator. Equipped with TV cameras and mechanical arms, it serves to explore the ocean bottom up to five miles off the California coast. (Scripps Institution of Oceanography)

23.—A view of the Russian atomic icebreaker *Lenin* under construction. With its three nuclear reactors, six steam generators, four steam turbines and eight dynamo engines this 44,000-h.p. flagship of the Russian fleet of icebreakers will be capable of staying at sea for eighteen months without putting into port. (Ullstein)

24.—The same picture reproduced with two different kinds of television camera tubes. Above, the conventional type; below, a recent tube which is much more sensitive to light than the human eye. With this tube it is possible to view fairly deep ocean regions without any searchlight glare. (General Electric Company)

25.—Deep-sea drillings have been made possible for the first time with the aid of CUSS I, a reconverted Navy barge. American scientists successfully pierced the so-called "second layer" of the ocean floor. In Mohole Project they will attempt to reach the earth's crust with the deepest hole ever drilled. (AMSOC)

26.—"Magic hands," here shown handling fragile Christmas tree decorations, will be installed on the outside of deep-sea submersibles. Manipulated from within the ship, they will be able to perform similar complicated and delicate tasks. (General Electric Company)

27.—A native of arid Kuwait drinks fresh water condensed from the waters of the Persian Gulf distilled by unit in the background. Its conversion capacity is 630,000 gallons per day. Bigger units are already being erected in the United States to counteract the growing water shortage. (Westinghouse Electric)

28.—Not a greenhouse, but another distilling plant. Salty sea water evaporates in these hot houses under Florida's burning sunshine. The condensation runs down the glass panes and is caught to give drinking water. (U.S. Office of Saline Water)

29.—An artist's impression of the city of the future. Enormous glass domes concentrate the sun's heat on an area of the sea, causing evaporation. Crystal-clear water, purified and drinkable, flows down the domes to be caught at the bottom in a gully. (Wide World)

University of West Berlin, holds a similar view: "One can only imagine people either starving in thousands or being forced to fight more and more vehemently to kill each other for food."

These gloomy outlooks have led many eminent scientists to urge that the growth rate of the world's population be regulated through birth control. The ethical pros and cons of this hotly disputed issue shall not concern us here, but, as a study of the Stanford Research Institute on population control states, "in a finite world some means of controlling population growth are inescapable." The study suggests that those governments and peoples that feel the problem of overpopulation to be acute should "speed up their quest for the physical, biological and social knowledge needed to check population growth by means other than disease, famine and war." (The traditional means of population control.)

Obviously, the upper limit of the earth's population does not so much depend on the "available standing room" on our planet, but on the amount of food that can be produced. Some studies, prepared decades ago and assuming a minimum food standard, set the world population at about three billion. Most recent studies estimate that the world could produce food for as many as seventeen billion people, provided that: all the lands at present unused or inadequately used are brought into production; new sources of food are discovered; synthesis of the basic components of human food and perhaps even the development of synthetic plants becomes possible; the oceans are effectively utilized.

Action to materialize some of these demands is urgently needed, for the population explosion and the threat of starvation already cast an ugly shadow over most of the so-called underdeveloped countries of the world. "In Africa one out of every three colored children dies of undernourishment before it is a year old, even at the present day. Many of those surviving this

toll perish before they are four," said a report of a scientific
investigation on the health of the colored children of South
Africa. Most adult Indians are worse off now, in spite of their
government's efforts to raise their standard of living, than they
were during their childhood. "Then we used to have two
meals a day. Now we are lucky if we get one," many of them
say.

Surprisingly, the food shortage in the underdeveloped nations has been brought about by—modern science. In its efforts
to reduce the death rate in these countries to "normal" out of
moral altruism, it neglected, however, to raise their economic
productivity at the same time. "The result," according to
Major General William H. Draper, chairman of former President Eisenhower's committee studying the program of military
aid, "is that food production simply cannot keep pace with the
speed at which the population grows in underdeveloped lands."
(To attain the urgently needed balance between economic
development and population growth, the Indian government is
already encouraging birth control through sterilization, while
Japan, in addition, has legalized abortions. Similar measures
have been taken by the governments of Java, Barbados, Mauritius, Egypt, mainland China and Puerto Rico.)

It is an irony of fate that so many die in lands of the Middle
and Far East precisely because they lack the very substance
surrounding them—protein. Almost all countries whose population suffers from a chronic deficiency of protein border
seas where fish are plentiful. For instance, the American research ship *Atlantis* had to plow its way through dense shoals
of tuna fish in the Red Sea, while only a few miles away
Egyptian fellahin were again going to bed hungry. In those
countries, generally only individual fishermen enjoy the nutritive value of animal protein. Fish is practically unknown on
the plateaus of Asia or South America, merely because of the
lack of economic and technical resources needed to procure

this valuable raw material from the sea. To overcome this difficulty one thing above all is needed: a program of planned fish consumption.

"Feeding most people," Sir Julian Huxley said at the beginning of November, 1959, "is determined by old customs. Millions of ignorant or prejudiced people have to be persuaded to alter their habits and bring them into line with modern knowledge." What Sir Julian meant was: "Eat more fish!"

In Morocco the first steps were taken in August, 1959, when government loudspeaker vans toured the suburbs of Rabat and Casablanca, not to blare out political promises but to announce what in the East amounted to revolutionary slogans. "Get as much nourishment from one and a half pounds of fish as you would from one pound of meat for only a quarter of the cost!" Most of the tin-hut dwellers in the suburbs of Rabat are peasants who have come from the central parts of the country in search of employment. They are so poor that only once in four or five months can they afford a sparse meat dinner; their main source of nourishment is watery vegetable soups with a little fat, which is why they lack proteins.

In the slum districts, the social welfare service erected stalls showing peasants how to prepare and cook fish. But that was not enough; they also had to prove to them that fish was edible! Fresh sardines were sold to paupers for ten cents a pound.

The government's measures, widely propagandized in movies, press and radio, had the desired effect. Not only did fish consumption rise; tradesmen were astonished to see how profitable it was to sell fish well below the usual Moslem racketeering prices. Shopkeepers were happy to see sales increase, as were the fishermen who benefited from the rising demand. In less than three hours over two tons of sardines were sold at a few stands where queues of two thousand people had formed. If this campaign is successful along the coast of Morocco, the doctrine of eating more fish should also spread to more central regions, which would mean the solution to a problem of national concern. It would not only provide the population with sufficient protein nourishment, but also boost the home fishing industry. Though Morocco possesses two thousand fishing craft, the total catch is nowhere near what it could be.

Countries other than Morocco are attempting to introduce fish consumption. In the autumn of 1959 some 120 Eskimos from northern central Canada were resettled along the coast when the threat of starvation hung over their heads. The caribou on which they lived were becoming extinct. Now missionaries and white settlers are instructing the Eskimos how to catch whales, walrus and sea trout. None has starved since they have begun to feed on the sea, and recently the natives have even been delivering these trout to towns situated in the south. From undernourished nomads they have been transformed into well-fed fishermen.

In the opinion of some scientists, an effort to whet the population's appetite for fish should also be made in Europe and America. "We inhabitants of Western countries wonder why people in underdeveloped countries don't like fish. We should make it clear that we aren't so crazy about it ourselves," they say. America's fishermen catch about three hundred different kinds of fish, yet 60 percent of the annual catch consists of no more than nine main species. The others have no market. The public will not eat anything to which it isn't accustomed. We shall therefore have to learn that not only herring, cod, tuna and flounder are tasty; so are countless others of the remaining twenty-five thousand species. But while the West will have to be encouraged to eat more fish, there is an essential difference between Europe and America on the one hand and the inhabitants of Asia, Africa and South America on the other. The former will merely have to accustom themselves to various new species; the latter will first have to be convinced that fish makes a nourishing meal.

Underdeveloped countries will have to build up their fishing industry. At present they catch only as much fish as they can sell; without means of refrigeration, the fish would rot after one hot day. Putting fish into cold storage (for which plants would first have to be erected) and transporting them by refrigerated trains (which would first have to be purchased) would send up the cost so much that the hungry inhabitants of the interior could not afford it after all. This vicious circle shows in small measure some of the difficulties that the developing lands are facing. They can only be overcome if the whole problem is tackled systematically from the start.

"We must show the coastal dwellers of those countries how to improve their methods of catching, to increase the haul. Then they will be able to sell fish cheaper, which will make storage and transport less expensive. If the settlers in the interior are enlightened in the way the Moroccans were, a higher fish consumption can be expected." That is what many economists maintain, and before long many countries may be pooling their experiences in this field, just as Japanese fishermen were instructing their Yugoslav colleagues in the skills of tuna fishing in the Adriatic during the summer of 1960.

In the United States and the countries of Europe, contrary to the underdeveloped nations, population increase and technical and economic progress have advanced together and still do. But the day is bound to come when Europe and the United States, instead of being able to export their food surpluses, as they do today, will require every ear of grain and every piece of meat, every potato and corn cob for their own growing population. For these reasons, the most urgent step (next to making more arid land available for agriculture) will be to cultivate the oceans of the world in order to raise food production. Managed properly, they could become the world's richest suppliers of food. It is easy to see why: only the top few inches of fields and meadows can be used for agricultural production. The oceans, on the other hand, could be cultivated for the same purpose down to far greater depths. Thus a given region in the sea could yield many times more than a surface of equal dimensions on land.

The NASCO report is the United States' first step toward investigating the oceans and fighting the threat of famine. It should provide the basis of a plan for developing the oceans, a plan which has by now become urgent. International cooperation would of course be needed to manage the world's seas successfully. The threat of hunger could provide the key to world peace, if all nations recognized that fact early enough to take common measures against it. Though such a concerted effort against the threat of hunger would amount to an enterprise unheard of in the history of mankind, it should be started immediately; otherwise those nations suffering most will one day resort to violence, when they see that it is too late for a planned exploitation of the seas. Battles will flare up everywhere in an effort to get at the last treasures of the earth as quickly and as easily as possible. The first signs of this danger —and they are signs which are hardly being heeded as yet— indicate how serious the situation may become.

9   The Fishing Wars

On the twenty-third of September, 1959, thick fog lay over the straits of Korea. It seemed as if it had been especially created for the sixty-nine-ton Japanese motor cutter *Myoei Maru*. Chugging along quietly it swayed to and fro a good sixty miles off the South Korean coast. Everything appeared to be going according to plan when suddenly heavy machine-gun fire whipped out of the fog causing consternation among the crew of the *Myoei Maru*. Out of the gray there then emerged the outline of a South Korean coastal patrol vessel, and the "Children of the Sun" were arrested shortly afterward. The cutter and its haul were seized and brought into a Korean port.

Politically Korea and Japan are Allied powers; yet they are involved in a most peculiar war: the booty in question is nothing other than fish.

The *Myoei Maru* with twenty tons of precious cargo on board was only one of many Japanese fishing vessels which have come into Korea's possession since 1952, when President Syngman Rhee decided offhandedly to extend Korean fishing boundaries to two hundred miles. Thus the 2,600 Japanese fishing craft in the process of depleting one of the world's richest fishing grounds were forbidden to stay in the new territorial waters claimed by Korea. Rhee regarded his measure as the only way of averting the danger threatening the popula-

tion of Korea and its national fishing industry, which is the
mainstay of Korea's economy. He had not considered that
his despotic step would have an almost catastrophic effect on
Japanese fishing, which suffered an annual loss of over $28
million with few prospects of improvement. That is how the
fishing war broke out. In spite of Rhee's prohibition Japanese
cutters continued their search for valuable prey in Korean
waters, while South Korean gunboats, faithful to their president's directions, accounted for some thirty Japanese boats
every year, interning up to four hundred Japanese fishermen
annually.

Japan failed in negotiations with South Korea to have the
fishing ban lifted. The only answer was to adopt similar
methods. Yasuji Watanabe, one of the most capable officers
in the Imperial Navy during the Second World War, was
commissioned to protect Japanese fishing craft from Korean
gunboats.

Watanabe had short-wave transmitters installed in all cutters. His own squadron's six speedboats, which carry no armaments, but merely radar, never stop patrolling in Korean
waters during the season. Immediately upon locating a Korean
gunboat a warning is transmitted to the nearest and most
jeopardized Japanese fishing craft, which haul in their nets
and immediately retire beyond the two-hundred-mile limit
until the danger has passed. Watanabe can smile; Japan has
already recovered one-third of her losses with his help. However, since November, 1960, his speedboats have been au-
thorized to fire at Korean gunboats should the latter move to
chase off or capture any Japanese vessels.

The fishing disagreement between Japan and Korea is
alarming, but what is worse is that it is not without parallel.
On May 30, 1961, the Danish frigate *Niels Ebbesen* fired three
sharp rounds at the British trawler *Red Crusader*, damaging
the craft. It then sent a prize commando on board to take over.

The Danes charged the British with fishing in Danish waters.

A similar dispute has existed between Great Britain and Iceland since 1958. On the first of September, 1958, Iceland decided to extend her territorial waters from four to twelve nautical miles. "This was necessary," explained David Olafsson, director of the Ministry of Fisheries, "because of the dangerous decrease in fish supplies around our country arising from excess fishing there." Britain refused to recognize Iceland's right in this matter, and sent her warships to protect her fishermen.

This caused the first incident on the second of September. In protest the British vessels *Northern Foam* and *Lifeguard* approached to within seven miles of the coast of Iceland. The Icelandic coastal patrols *Thor* and *Maria Julia*, which tried to hinder them, were driven back under threat of gunfire. Frigates of the Royal Navy ensured that British boats could fish unmolested within the twelve-mile fishing zone, much to the annoyance of the Icelanders, until the dispute was finally settled in February, 1961. The British can now fish within the twelve-mile zone at certain times and only with the express permission of the Icelandic government.

The size of the annual catch is an important factor in Iceland's existence, as it is in Korea's: 95 percent of all her exports consist of fish or allied products. The yield has been on the decline for years. Ironically enough, it was a British report on fishing around Iceland that stated: "Cod fishing in 1958 brought in little more than the previous year in spite of more intense efforts. The haul per boat has dropped considerably. . . . The catch in 1959 will probably be even worse." This fear proved to be true.

In fact, the total catch by all large fishing fleets has been dropping from year to year. In many cases the haul in traditional fishing grounds is so slight that many fishermen consider it hardly worthwhile any longer.

In 1928 the large Boston fleet brought in 200 million pounds of haddock. Thirty years later the catch amounted to only 70 million pounds, the worst in thirty-six years. In 1953 the vast sardine industry on America's West Coast almost went bankrupt. For years 600,000 tones of sardines had been processed; then suddenly without warning in 1953 the haul shrank to a ridiculous five thousand tons.

On the northwest coast of America right up to Alaska much of the economy depends on the size of the annual salmon catch. Even here the future looks dim. Although intensified methods of catching have been tried, the yield continues to fall. In 1959 it was 40 percent lower than in 1958, which was itself a bad year. Whereas some three million crates were packed with salmon in the latter year, in 1959 the total was down to a mere 1,700,000.

Canadian fishermen are also very concerned about the prospects. Although the haul is still good and sufficient, they fear that this state of affairs will not last. "There have already been indications," they say. "Nowadays we have to stay out for several weeks before we can return with full holds. Ten years ago we would have had more than three hundred tons of fish in the boat after one week."

If this situation does not change, the outcome is obvious. The demand for fish by modern industry and by the growing world population will not decrease. In fact, more fish will be needed. Since all Western countries are experiencing a decline in the size of their catch, most of them will have to fill the gap between supply and demand with increased fish imports from countries living on fish exports. However, the day will come when even the latter, such as Japan and Korea, will have to limit their exports for the sake of their own consumption. What then?

In his State of the Union Message, President Kennedy stated that by 1980 the United States would need an additional three billion pounds of fish and shellfish annually to meet her nutritional needs. This represents a 60 percent increase of the total 1960 U.S. catch, though this year the haul is again declining rather than increasing. The additional quantity needed in 1980 can hardly be raised by imports, as is generally recognized.

The only solution is to double the present catch in the course of the next twenty years. The big question is: how? How can more fish be caught when the stocks in the Seven Seas appear to be dwindling? Only oceanographers, whose advice in the past has so often been ridiculed by fishermen, can give the answer. The fact that Western governments are gradually beginning to support the work of their oceanographers is proof enough that their truly vital work is finally receiving the recognition it deserves.

On the other hand, the Russian government has for many years recognized what oceanography can do for its fishing industry. While the Western fish catches dwindle from year to year, Russia's catches are constantly increasing. Her fishermen off the coast of Newfoundland are now taking in ten times more fish than New England rivals who have worked the shoals for years. They are also hauling in great amounts of fish off the coasts of South Africa and Japan and are now moving into the Indian Ocean. The latest available figure for Russian fish catches in 1959 is 6.8 million pounds, as compared to our catch of 4.8 million pounds in 1960. This means that the Russian catch increased by almost 700 million pounds in two years, while our own has been declining.

How do they do it? Part of the explanation lies in the ever-increasing size of the Soviet fishing fleet, which trebled between 1954 and 1959. Today it is the world's largest and most modern oceangoing fishing fleet, exceeding that of the United States by five to one.

Three hundred and fifty to 450 cutters from the U.S.S.R.

and her satellite states are now cruising in the North Atlantic, while in June, 1960, the Kremlin granted a further sum of $280 million to enlarge the fleet even more. Some seventy new factory ships, for instance, will be ordered from East Germany and Poland to be used for fishing in the tropics. Equipped with refrigerating plants, they are mainly for sardine, herring and tuna fishing. In comparison, the United States, Spain and Norway were at that time only beginning to order their first new factory ships in many years. At present, West Germany has eight and Great Britain six—an amazingly small and insufficient number.

In 1959, an act was passed by the Massachusetts legislature granting assistance to the New Bedford fishing industry, once the largest in the country but now "in serious difficulties and on the point of extinction." By 1963 a large number of new boats are to be built with state and federal aid, although the money would not have been granted had it not been that someone suggested designing the ships so that they could be used for defense purposes if necessary.

Yet merely raising the numbers of boats or fleets, as fishery experts well know, is only a stopgap measure. The total catch is increased, but this method is costly as the catch per vessel remains relatively low. More economical and efficient methods than net fishing have been suggested, beginning with "electrofishing" and going on to "fish dredges," which draw herring straight into the holds. These projects have already been realized in part, mainly by the Russians.

"But even fish dredges are not the final solution. With them we would only deplete the old fishing grounds even more quickly!" said a spokesman of the American NASCO program. "Before we start on newfangled methods of fishing, we have to learn something about the fish themselves."

Fortunately, marine biologists tell us that the drop in the world's fishing catch does not mean that the oceans' reserves are already getting low, but rather that large schools of herring, cod, salmon and tuna have sought out new quarters in the sea. Searches are therefore proceeding under the auspices of various nations to locate these new quarters. But what is so far happening is that we hunt, rather than raise, fish. We still catch them where we find them and without sufficient planning, in ignorance of their habits and in total disregard of the consequences of indiscriminate or overfishing. A correct and sound use of the ocean's resources makes it mandatory not only to look for new fishing grounds and use more efficient fishing gear, but to assure the constant replenishment of existing fish stock first.

We will therefore have to answer many questions before we can fish scientifically. How many fish are there in the ocean? Where do they live? Where do they spawn? How do they develop, and when and why do they die? Do we catch them at the right age or in the correct season? Our fishermen are never certain whether they will find fish in the same place as they did the previous year, or whether they will have to start searching afresh. We must investigate thoroughly the conditions affecting different species of fish. If we were better acquainted with their habits we should be able to predict with a fair degree of accuracy year by year whether individual shoals would leave a certain area and where they might go.

To study all these questions marine biologists have already proposed a system of large, manned buoys drifting or anchored on the high seas. Like vertical cylinders, they would rise several stories above the surface, and extend three hundred feet below it. The laboratories, at different levels below the water line, would be walled in by thick glass windows through which the marine life of various layers could be observed. Once again "magic hands" would protrude from the buoy's walls to seize samples of water and plankton and to make necessary measurements. The stories above water would be for accommodation and wireless rooms; those below, the laboratories for generators, batteries, fuel tanks, storage of provisions, refrigerator plants and aquariums. Every buoy would be equipped with a midget submarine, while the roof of the top story could act as a landing field for helicopters. The cost per buoy is estimated at approximately $2.5 million. The ideal buoy, of course, would be a tubular tower reaching from the ocean floor to far above the waves.

While marine biologists continue to plan for their ideal buoy, the Office of Naval Research has commissioned a West Coast company to construct a more modest drifting laboratory, nicknamed Flip, short for Floating Instrument Platform. It will be used mainly for secret research in antisubmarine warfare. However, it could at any time be used for research in marine biology. Ready in 1962, this 355-foot long tube will accommodate four men.

Modern vessels developed from military submarines will also soon be used to continue the direct observation of shoals of fish, since the methods employed so far have by no means been satisfactory. For some years marine biologists have been marking scores of fish with small plastic tabs on which the date and position of the catch are recorded. They are then let loose, and surprisingly large numbers of them fall once more into the hands of fishermen—often years later—in regions far distant from where they were originally caught. The fishermen then deliver the tab to marine biologists, informing them of the date and place of the recent catch. In a new process first tested in America in 1960, young fish are stamped with tiny, slightly radioactive metal plates, carrying a code number. As soon as the marked fish are recaptured special detectors seek them out on the conveyer to the processing machines. As we know where the fish was caught, we can determine how far it traveled since its first capture.

Effective as the above methods may seem, they are by no means ideal. Although we can determine how far the fish journeyed, we are still in doubt about the exact course it traveled, which is just what marine biologists and ichthyologists would like to know. It was therefore suggested in both the U.S. and Russia that midget submarines should follow individual shoals on their annual migrations. They could keep far enough away from the fish not to irritate them, and yet keep on their track by the use of sonars and hydrophones.

Jacques-Yves Cousteau's diving vessel *Denise* is a step in this direction. Two divers lie on foam-rubber mattresses inside the lens-shaped vessel, from which they can observe a shoal of fish through two portholes for twenty hours. The *Denise* is propelled by electric batteries and high-pressure pumps, which draw in water to expel it again forcibly in jets. It can attain a depth of fifteen hundred feet, but Cousteau already has a second one in mind which will have twice this diving capacity.

Using these or similar kinds of vessels, it would be possible to discover the reason why fish gradually or suddenly disappear from fishing grounds. It is now supposed that the reasons for this can be traced to changes in the courses of ocean currents. These changes can arise from weather conditions deviating strongly from their normal pattern or from seaquakes. Some scientists also believe that fish learn by experience, and so are gradually disappearing from favorite fishing areas. Cousteau has this to say: "Fish can learn. A few years ago they were quite friendly under water. Now they keep well away from divers with harpoons; the longer the harpoon, the further away they remain!"

Dr. H. O. Bull, an English oceanographer of the Dover Maritime Laboratory, believes that this is true not only of individual fish, but of whole schools. In a series of experiments with several hundred codfish kept in an aquarium, the fish swam up quickly when sonar impulses were sent through the water and food was thrown in at the same time.

Dr. Bull concluded from this observation that some fish

(just like many other animals) are indeed endowed with hearing sensitive to high-frequency impulses. However, if they (as in the above-mentioned experiment) are intelligent enough to connect the impulses with the imminence of food, they may also be able automatically to connect danger with sonar impulses in the freedom of nature. Dr. Bull thinks that sonars will therefore eventually give way to hydrophones, which pick up underwater sound instead of generating it. Fish will then attract fishermen with the noise they themselves create—instead of being chased away by man-made noise.

Dr. Bull's unusual theory that fish learn by experience still needs thorough investigation. One thing, however, is definite: it is chiefly the movement of the ocean's waters that causes the fish to take certain courses to other areas of the sea. This fact has been learned in the past by countries hard hit by fish migrations. For example, in 1935, an enormous whirlpool formed in the cold Kuroshio current which flows along the Japanese coast; it was almost 125 miles in diameter. Its effect was to drive the fish from the usual fishing grounds. The weather suddenly turned so warm in the northerly Japanese islands no longer touched by the cold current that the farmers there were able to take up rice cultivation. The miracle lasted for "seven years of plenty"; then the eddy disappeared as suddenly as it had come, and the Kuroshio current again flowed in its old course. The results were catastrophic: the rice harvest dropped off lamentably, while fishermen returned home empty-handed.

Abrupt changes of this kind occur in the currents of all the world's oceans. If they could be foreseen in time—which might be possible after sufficient study and observation—the necessary precautions could be taken to preserve the economic life in the coastal districts of the lands thus hit. The mysterious appearance and disappearance of large shoals of sardines off the coast of southern California have been causing oceanographers and marine biologists headaches for many years. They believe this phenomenon to be due to temperature and current changes in the Pacific, but at present they have insufficient means and too little information at their disposal to be able to predict these alterations in advance.

Jack Marr, biologist of the U.S. Fish and Wildlife Service, adds to this that "in the high season between 150 and 180 thousand tons of sardines were caught annually. In 1949, the catch fell to 40,000 tons and in 1951 reached a new low of 15,000 tons. Not until 1958 did the haul begin to rise again, so that today it is about 30,000 tons." While the ups and downs of the total catch were being noted, it was established that the size of the catch was affected by the rise and fall of the water temperature. Whether, as in the case of sardines, warm temperatures entice more fish into an area or whether the mortality rate of the spawn is lower at that time is one of the many problems that marine biologists are trying to solve.

As more and more knowledge about the various factors influencing the behavior and migration of fish is gained, marine biologists will be able to prepare so-called fish atlases for various ocean areas. Just as today's maps show the most important currents and some ocean topography, these fish atlases will, in addition, indicate all factors which appear to influence the behavior of shoals, and will contain relevant data about temperatures and sediments on the ocean floor. Physical and chemical conditions of the water in varying regions will also be noted. The chief innovation will be the inclusion of information about the distribution, density and reproduction rate of the microscopic plant and animal life called, respectively, phytoplankton and zooplankton. Aided by these data marine biologists will be able to predict with greater accuracy than at present not merely the most promising fishing grounds but the prospective size of individual shoals as well.

Work on a North Atlantic fish atlas already began early

in 1960. It will record not only where shoals worth catching normally reside, but also where they may be found according to weather and season. Even those areas which may be cultivated in the future will be marked.

An international headquarters, in which all the readings from observation buoys, exploration vessels and fishing craft can be pooled and evaluated, is the goal of the future. In coming years fish atlases and suggestions concerning fishing grounds will be sent at regular intervals before and during the season to individual fleets just as weather charts are transmitted by cable to all interested parties today.

The origins of this development go back to 1901, when the International Council of Oceanography was founded, with headquarters in Copenhagen and delegates from nine countries. Here news or information about fishing, fishing grounds and oceanography in northwest Europe is exchanged for the common good. A similar body, the North American Fishing Council, exists in the U.S., and under the direction of the Food and Agriculture Organization there are unions of fishing nations for the Mediterranean, South America and the western Pacific, all with similar objects.

However, what the scientists of all these countries need in order to apply their knowledge of fish life most fruitfully on a large scale is not merely the genuine support of fishermen, but financial and moral help and cooperation from their governments. Often, however, it seems that each land is concerned only with itself and its advantages, and refuses to make any sacrifice for the good of other nations (e.g., limiting the annual catch of its own fleet to a given maximum). Nevertheless, several nations have already made agreements to protect the existing fish, in the North Sea and the Baltic, for instance, where excessive fishing is no longer allowed. Perhaps the time will come when an authority under the UN will be established along the lines of these smaller organizations to allocate fishing grounds and quotas to the fleets of various nations, as is happening in whaling today. Then a new, urgently needed branch of fishing will come into being, to organize fishing strategy and put an end to planless and selfish competition. Different countries' fleets will operate according to precise data previously computed at a committee table telling where fish can and may be caught in the shortest possible time. In such a way all warfare over fish may be eliminated.

Japanese oceanographers have demonstrated how advantageous it is nowadays for a nation to keep an eye on the temperature of the water, its plankton content and the changing courses of ocean currents. Their research was decisive in maintaining their national fishing industry and keeping the islands' inhabitants alive. Almost 80 percent of the population's protein is provided by fish. They had no problem before World War II, when Japan led the world's fishing nations. However, for many years after 1945 Japan was forbidden by the victorious powers to fish in the old grounds off the Russian, American and Australian coasts, and her cutters were banned from the stretch of water extending the length of Canada, Red China and Korea.

The annual catch had already fallen to a dangerous level when in the fifties Japanese oceanographers began measuring the currents in all areas on the open seas (that is, those outside the jurisdiction of the Allied sea powers) which appeared favorable to fishing. They knew that tuna, their chief catch, preferred certain currents. So they recorded air and sea temperatures with scrupulous care and traced the presence of various types of plankton. Where several favorable factors converged, they expected, according to previous experience, to discover fish. And, indeed, their laborious, expensive work was soon rewarded.

Beginning at traditional fishing grounds the oceanographers followed every known and newly discovered ocean current in their research ships. By the summer of 1957, they had come upon nine new grounds replete with tuna. One year later Japan's fish harvest had already surpassed her prewar peak by 900,000 tons (twenty times as much as was caught in the Baltic in the same year).

The new tuna grounds discovered by the Japanese number among the richest in the world and are being exploited by various South American nations, France and Spain. Intensive oceanographic research has also led to the discovery of vast shoals of perch in the North Pacific and large herds of the much sought king crab in Bering Strait.

All this goes to show that it is still possible to discover many new shoals of fish in the oceans, perhaps in regions where, owing to the lack of oceanographic data, there were thought to be no signs of their presence. Such areas could easily be in the immediate vicinity of Asia's starving nations or near those lands dependent on fish imports. Australia, for example, will be importing less since marine biologists discovered extensive new fishing grounds off the country's northwest coast in 1959.

Not only are new fishing grounds coming to light, but man is discovering that fish, which have until now been thought to live, and were therefore hunted, exclusively in the upper regions of the water, also subsist at much greater depths. Various kinds of "surface" fish have been found in the stomachs of sperm whales, which seek their food at a depth of almost 2,500 feet. Saber fish have been caught at depths of between two and four thousand feet, although formerly they were supposed to be found only in the upper regions.

Dr. George Humphrey, director of the Department of Fishing and Oceanography in the Australian National Research Council, has declared: "Certainly there is enough fish in the world for everyone. But instead of expending their energy on snatching the fattest scraps away from each other, fishing nations should start examining the life and abode of the large shoals, and then think about how to distribute them."

There is now no doubt that this will actually happen in the course of the next few years, on the basis of observations carried out in every ocean. An enormous expenditure would be necessary, if temperature and current readings were taken by manned vehicles in the different seas. For that reason American oceanographers have proposed the building of two hundred unmanned, automatic observation buoys, costing a mere seventeen million dollars, to be launched in the most important areas for the drawing up of fish charts. With the aid of a small atomic generator, which transforms the radiant heat of a radioactive isotope into electricity, their transmitters can send out continuous readings similar to those on board artificial satellites. Another possibility to guarantee the continued functioning of the transmitter is a small generating station powered by wave motion. The buoys could also register changing wind speed, the height of the waves and the salt content of the water. All information would be stored on magnetic tape. Aircraft flying along the chain of buoys at regular intervals could call off the data from the tape recorder. The tape in each individual buoy would then automatically be erased to start immediately recording new information. Other buoys could be used to measure underwater currents. After they had descended to predetermined depths, research submarines could take their readings by remote control.

As a further aid, artificial satellites could give precise information on the presence and exact course of cold and warm currents, desired by meteorologists, oceanographers and marine biologists. Such satellites will be equipped with an instrument especially sensitive to infrared rays, i.e., to heat. From a height of 350 miles they could detect the slightest variations in the temperature of the areas of the sea over which they pass, and they would have no problem in locating warm currents in cold areas and vice versa. These observations would be transmitted to corresponding ground stations. Oceanographers will thus be able to determine any change in the course of the currents, and take all necessary measures to warn interested parties. At the same time one orbit of a satellite will yield more information about temperature zones than has as yet been accessible to a fleet of research ships.

However, it is not only changes in the horizontal currents that force fish to move to new areas in the ocean. Of almost equal importance is the surge of the vertical current which rises from the depths of the ocean, bringing with it minerals, phosphates and nitrates from the sea floor. These substances, by-products of the continual erosion of the continents, are washed out to sea by the rivers of the world. They are supplemented by the remains of decaying marine plant and animal life, of the utmost importance to phytoplankton, which would practically starve without them. Where this current is lacking there is little or no phytoplankton and therefore no large shoals of fish, for zooplankton feeds on phytoplankton, and small crustaceans and young fish live on both. Thus one depends on the other, and at the end of this "food chain" we have the big fish, which are becoming more and more vital to us.

The most recent plan, therefore, is to increase these vertical currents in the seas of the world, or to create them artificially where they do not exist. Thus man will eventually plow the oceans to increase their fertility.

10 Fish Farms and Nuclear Reactors

Members of the National Academy of Sciences Committee on Oceanography are giving careful thought to an amazing project: the sinking of a nuclear reactor at a selected spot in the sea. This atomic oven could provide sufficient heat to warm the cold water of the deep, which would then start to rise to the surface. The artificially created vertical circulation would carry the nutrient minerals contained in the depths to the upper, three hundred-foot sunlit layer of the sea, where they would help to support the growth of phytoplankton, which in turn would attract large schools of fish. In this way, new fishing grounds could be created. The NASCO report states that "the Committee considers the idea promising enough to recommend that grants be given, first for feasibility studies, then for detailed engineering developments of promising proposals, and finally for pilot scale trials of devices which are developed."

The ocean is like a vast continent. It contains "forests" of seaweed and possesses lush pastures where plankton, the "green fodder" of the sea, abounds. These pastures—where up to five million cells of plankton have been counted in one quart of water—constitute the richest fishing grounds of our planet. On the open sea they are limited to areas where vertical upwelling

currents plow up nutrients from the sea floor. More of them
are to be found on the continental shelves, the belts of comparatively shallow water surrounding most land masses. Often
the pastures can be recognized from the air, as their water is a
dull green when breaking in waves.

Of course, the ocean also contains zones with comparatively
little marine life, such as the regions in the eastern Pacific and
the mid-Atlantic. Finally, there are so-called ocean "deserts."
Their water is of a clear, almost transparent blue, as in large
areas of the Mediterranean. These regions have almost no upwelling and are only crossed by weak surface currents which
do not introduce enough nutrients from other regions. Little
phytoplankton can be found in the ocean's deserts, seldom more
than ten thousand cells per quart of water. Their reproduction
rate is so slight that sufficient quantities never become available
as food for fish. Consequently fish reproduction in these regions stays limited.

In certain fertile areas of the ocean, the upwelling can sometimes cease abruptly. As a result, the reproduction of phytoplankton in that area will come to a virtual standstill. Fish die
or move away to "greener pastures," and, as a result, the fishing industry of a nation can be seriously affected. This has
frequently happened in Peru, for instance.

Off the coast of that South American country flows the
Humboldt Current. On its shoreward side are countless eddies
which, together with the prevailing coastal winds, create strong
upwellings in that particular area. The nutrition-laden waters
that rise to the surface allow the plankton to thrive—and so do
the millions of anchovies, small sardine-like fish. But every so
often—the last time in 1956–57—the Humboldt Current moves
out to sea. The upwelling ceases—with disastrous results. Not
only do the local fishermen have a meager catch but another
branch of industry—the guano trade—also suffers, for Peru's
fishermen are not the only hunters of anchovies. Some thirty

million sea birds feed upon them as well. The 300,000 tons of bird dung they annually produce (which means that they devour about four million tons of anchovies per year) is a most valuable fertilizer. When the reproduction of anchovies drops due to the lack of food, the birds starve by the millions, considerably reducing the production rate of guano.

Turning the unfruitful regions of the sea into fat pastures by means of nuclear reactors lowered to the bottom is not the only proposal of the Committee on Oceanography. Mechanical means of producing vertical circulations were discussed by Richard Vetter, the committee's executive secretary. He suggested hanging a mammoth chain somewhere halfway between Miami and Cuba into the deep-reaching Florida current. The top end of the chain could be attached to buoys floating on the surface, the lower end anchored firmly on the sea floor. Large sheets of metal similar to the blades of a ventilator would be attached horizontally to the chain. The deep current would set the lower blades into motion, and a revolving movement would continue up the chain. Like the agitator of an enormous washing machine the metal blades would stir up the water, creating an upward current. Nutrients would no longer be swept away by the deep-flowing Florida current, but would rise to the surface, creating a new "pasture." As the Florida current is also part of the Gulf Stream the rising nutrients might also reach other regions of the sea. By planting a number of "super-agitators" in the right places, deserts in the North and mid-Atlantic could be turned into fruitful pastures.

What could be done to keep an agitator in motion in areas where there is no horizontal current? Here the temperature differences themselves as they exist in the ocean would be enlisted to help. By a simple principle of physics they could pump the cold water from the depths to the surface. Man only has to give this process a working start. A model of the device to make the pumping action possible is in preparation at the laboratory of the Woods Hole Oceanographic Institution. In a regular "field test" a plastic pipe would be lowered down through the temperature boundary into the cold depths. With a little pumping the cold water could be made to rise slowly up the pipe. The nearer it got to the surface, the warmer it would become, losing density in the process. Moreover, as water from the depths has a lower salinity than surface water, it would become almost weightless in the pipe. As its buoyancy increased, the water would start to flow like an artesian well. The pumps could then be shut off, for the water would continue to rise up the pipe automatically, emptying all its nutrients into what was formerly an ocean desert. As long as the water deep down is colder than that on the surface, and as long as normal weather conditions prevail, this vertical current would keep flowing.

The idea described above was put forward as early as 1954 by Bodo Schillat, a mechanical engineer in Hamburg, but got no response. Only about six years later, America's oceanographers began intensively investigating this and similar methods to plow the ocean. Columbus Iselin of Woods Hole has suggested laying a number of perforated pipes on the floor of the St. Lawrence River Delta in Canada. By continuously pumping air through the pipes, millions of bubbles would rise through the small holes to the surface, not only carrying up the nutritious elements, but also helping to keep the river delta free of ice during the winter months.

Another method to raise fish reproduction in the ocean would be to enrich certain regions with phosphates and nitrogen. This is precisely what the Russians are planning to do in the near future. Since the open sea naturally would demand exorbitant supplies of artificial manure, fertilizing would be limited mainly to bays and inlets. An experiment by the American Fish and Wildlife Service (conducted in a pond to ensure better control) impressively indicates what results can be expected from artificial fertilization of water bodies. The pond was thoroughly cleaned and then scientifically enriched with trace elements and phosphates. The results were amazing. Whereas for a long time the water had yielded only three pounds of trout per acre, it now produced 179 pounds in the same area.

In Manila Bay fish and shrimp are already being raised on so-called fish farms where the larvae are fed soya flour, maize and barley. In this way, it is hoped to make up part of the lack of protein suffered from in the Philippines.

American oceanographers believe that trace elements, and chemical nutrients such as phosphates and nitrogen, are not the only chemical nutrients that increase the growth of phytoplankton. Apparently these can be supplemented by other matter contained in sea water in the minute concentration essential not only to plant growth, but also to the growth, feeding rates and survival of animals. Were it possible to identify a certain "substance X," isolate it and prove its beneficial effect on marine life, it might be possible to extract the same matter from the soil of continents and "inject" it into ocean areas where the rate of plankton growth is very small. In such a way a new science called marine agronomy would begin.

Professor Lev Senkyevitch, marine biologist of the Moscow Academy of Sciences, believes that man will undertake "extensively organized, well-arranged ocean farming in the next century." In the same way that agriculture is subdivided into diverse branches, e.g., cattle raising, vegetable farming and forestry, men will have to subdivide the science of marine agronomy into varied branches throughout the ocean. The fishing industries of the larger nations could then set up regular cultivation programs in which not only the harvest but also the annual fertilizing and canalizing of certain areas of the ocean could be preplanned. Oceanographic institutes throughout the world are already making decisive contributions in this direction.

Scientific expeditions of the Oceanographic Institute in

Edinburgh, for instance, have analyzed the composition of plankton in different parts of the North Sea in order to gain precise information on the different species and number of fish populating a particular area. From the number of fish eggs in a certain amount of sea water marine biologists can tell the approximate size of the spawning school of fish, while the color of the plankton in the sample indicates the type of fish. A certain species of red plankton, for instance, provides the main source of nourishment for herring. Marine biologists can also determine the chances of survival of any particular breed of fish by comparing the number of fish larvae in a water sample with the number of fertilized eggs previously derived from a similar water sample of the same area. From this they can calculate the quantity of fish to be expected in that particular region in coming seasons.

Collecting and analyzing plankton samples in all areas of the ocean will help marine biologists to understand the distribution and amount of certain species of fish. R. S. Glover of the Edinburgh Institute, who has already analyzed some fifty thousand samples from widely differing zones of the northeast Atlantic and the North Sea since 1950, is compiling a plankton atlas of these areas. The atlas should be of great assistance to future fishing fleets, helping them to find the locations where fish thrive most easily and in greatest quantity.

Further advanced is a project of the American Geographical Society, in which a *Serial Atlas of the Marine Environment* of the Atlantic from the North Pole to the Equator is being compiled. The monumental project will draw a total picture of these maritime areas, and their nonliving and living resources. Dr. Revelle of the Scripps Institution of Oceanography is convinced that there will one day be an agency forecasting the presence and migrations of large fields of plankton in the same way as national meteorological offices now predict cloud formations. These readings would be entered annually in atlases and fish charts. Since fish follow the drifting plankton, by looking at a plankton chart fishermen will be able to tell with more certainty than today where to find their prey.

All this clearly indicates the extreme importance of plankton in ocean farming. But just as man is beginning to realize the significance of this minute marine life, he seems to be making the first steps toward its destruction. In recent years there has been more and more talk of making the sea a dumping ground for radioactive waste. No one can yet say with assurance whether the effect of this dumping is really as harmless as some members of the Atomic Energy Commission maintain, or whether the radioactive waste will not contribute to the annihilation of the microscopic plankton and with it the fish as well. In this respect much careful study is still necessary to prevent man's setting up a vicious circle which could lead to his own destruction, for the sea is in the final instance the last food source on earth. Simultaneously with research in this field, it will also be necessary to protect certain existing marine organisms (such as whales) from dangerous overfishing, and their reproduction rates will have to be increased wherever possible.

The ocean offers plenty of space in which billions of creatures can thrive. The whole human race could be fed from the seas if they were farmed scientifically, i.e., at various levels and by bringing the regions as yet undeveloped under the oceanographer's plow. Therefore, it is planned not only to make the ocean deserts fertile with giant agitators and nuclear reactors, but also to introduce certain species of fish into areas where they were hitherto unknown. Large-scale fish farms also could be established off the coasts of certain countries, and shelters in which different kinds of fish would be kept like cattle in sheds could be erected on the sea floor.

The English space scientist, Arthur C. Clarke, in one of his science fiction books, *Deep Range*, describes life under water in the year 2060. Manned midget submarines proceeding from a parent ship act as "sheep dogs" to keep schools of whales together. "Whale boys," or men serving in these submarines under the supervision of a World Food Organization, carry out practically the same job under water as their cowboy counterparts on land. They watch over the whales, herd them together in one area, and when necessary hunt down the number needed for meat. The vessels they use are the logical end product of the military midget submarines we mentioned earlier in this book. They possess a whole arsenal of weapons, tools and scientific instruments; "branding irons" are used to mark painlessly those whales that will not attach themselves to the school voluntarily and therefore need special attention; to kill the required number of sea mammals, tiny torpedoes and poisonous darts are fired from the ship.

The idea of keeping fish in enclosures is by no means absurd. In England people are thinking of laying electric cables at the entrance to large bays. The weak voltage would act as a wall in the water which the fish could not penetrate, forcing them to remain in the bay. Successful experiments have been carried out in America using several perforated pipes which send up a curtain of air bubbles from the sea floor. Once herrings and sardines are surrounded by this wall they will not swim through it. By creating noise underwater, for instance, it is possible to chase them to the edge and there simply draw them out of the water with suction devices.

Another plan foresees marine life seeking out and then staying in special "stalls" intended for them, much as cattle do on farms. Its originator is none other than Jacques-Yves Cousteau, who, among other things, is the director of the famous oceanographic museum in Monaco. Cousteau frequently noticed on his many dives how certain sea creatures soon congregate wherever a ship has sunk, whereas the immediate surroundings appear to be deserted. Perhaps, he reasoned, fish prefer to lead a "sheltered" life. His next thought was as logical as it sounds amazing: why wasn't it possible systematically to breed certain sea creatures, just like farm animals, until they are ready to be slaughtered? The only condition would be to provide a "stable" where they could settle in sufficient quantities, for only when they had congregated in a confined space would reaping be worthwhile.

For the purpose of ecological studies, Cousteau designed a shelter with several stories for fish and other inhabitants of the deep. He has named his concrete building the Biatron. Each floor has been equipped for a particular species. One, for instance, will be installed with plenty of tubes and holes, living quarters preferred by eels. The first Biatrons are to be constructed right in front of the museum in Monaco on a section of the sea bed three miles wide. While certain experimental shelters will be made of concrete, Cousteau will build others of synthetic materials, to find which ones are the most suitable. Cousteau estimates the best depth at which these "stables" should be placed to be between one and four hundred feet.

Between the Biatrons there will be illuminated "roads" to attract the fish and simplify the work of the underwater fishermen. Chemical nutrients will be distributed from house to house by means of pipes, and Cousteau hopefully is looking toward the day when skin-diving marine farmers will be working in large fish stables under water if the studies should show the expected results. The ring-shaped atolls in the South Seas, for instance, would be eminently suitable for such a purpose, especially if deep-sea water, rich in nutrients, could be pumped in.

However utopian all this may sound, it is not far from realization. At the end of this century fish will be caught where it suits the fishermen, not, as is the case today, where the fish decide to go. Eighty years ago a small start was made in this direction when people tried to introduce exotic fish in regions where there was a deficiency of them.

Around 1880 a large number of shad, a member of the herring family, were brought from the East Coast of the U.S. to the West Coast. Eight years later, 100,000 pounds of shad were caught off the California coast, and today the annual catch of this species in California waters totals some four million pounds. Similarly, the Chinook salmon of North America has been established in New Zealand.

Naturally, not all of the earliest transplantation experiments were so successful as the ones described above, mainly due to lack of suitable water conditions in the areas to which the fish had been introduced. Today, with more knowledge on marine life and its environment, oceanographers are once again giving increased attention to this procedure. Some of the most important lectures during the 1959 Oceanographic Congress in New York were those given by English and Russian scientists which dealt with the introduction of certain species of fish for which there is a great demand in regions far from their native habitat.

The English have been experimenting since 1920 with young flounders, bringing them in canisters to the plankton-filled waters around the British Isles. The fish were allowed time to grow, and, after it had become clear that the flounders were reproducing prolifically, fishermen could cast their nets in these areas. The Russians, on the other hand, are introducing herring from northern waters to the regions near the Antarctic which are poor in fish life.

Introduction of marine organisms into new ocean areas cannot be successfully undertaken on a larger scale, however, until we know with certainty all the environmental factors that affect the growth and survival of young fish. It is useless to try to raise a larger number of fish in ocean farms as long as we have no means of protecting them from their natural enemies, and from various diseases that could kill off entire schools. Help in this field will have to come from marine biologists who are already actively engaged in identifying fish diseases and discovering what to do about them.

11   Sick Fish

In October of 1959 the waves of the Gulf of Mexico washed up tens of thousands of dead fish onto the white beaches of Florida. With every new high tide an extra heap of cadavers was piled up over a hundred-mile-long stretch of the coast. The sun's rays beat down mercilessly, turning the famous holiday-makers' paradise into a stinking hell. Tourists stayed away and many a frustrated landlady was desperately waving her vacancy sign. What caused this plague was the so-called "red tide," more precisely the protozoa, *Gymnodinium brevis*. This single-celled, rust-brown creature is harmless as long as the prevalent ocean conditions are unfavorable to its reproduction in enormous numbers. But in the fall of 1959 (and once before in the autumn of 1957) it had been unusually sultry in Florida; at the same time, there had been tropical rainstorms over the peninsula, which softened the phosphate soil and washed it out to sea. Thus *Gymnodinium*, which uses the phosphate in a similar way a plant uses fertilizer, began to reproduce at an accelerated pace. It was not long before large expanses of water in the Gulf of Mexico took on a rust-brown shade, sometimes extending in bands of twenty miles or more. Waves slimy with the secretion from billions of these creatures flopped sluggishly onto the beach. The secretion had a poisonous effect on fish. The animals affected by the "red tide" rose to the surface, whirled crazily about for a while, turned on their sides and died. Even people onshore were affected in a peculiar way: with an onshore wind, their eyes burned, their throats became sore and their nostrils were irritated.

In 1962 there was still no definite way of predicting the outbreak of a "red tide." Nor do we know how to exterminate the creature or prevent its reproduction without endangering the vital plankton. The only thing that has any effect at the moment is cooler weather—and less phosphorus in the water.

Fishermen and marine biologists are equally powerless against many other ocean plagues which sporadically crop up throughout the world. One of them is the so-called "sputnik grass," which nothing at the moment seems able to stop. This spongelike algae, usually found only in the salt-water inlets of Scandinavia, suddenly appeared in the shallow, briny bays of Connecticut toward the end of 1957, shortly after the launching of the first Soviet space satellite which gave the algae their name. Already they cover thousands of acres at the bottom of many of Long Island's bays. As the sputnik grass continued to spread at a frightening rate, fish started to leave the bays, since the algae use up all the nutrients in the water. They also cover the scallop so that it cannot swim and sinks to the bottom. Long Island fishermen who depend on a good scallop catch for a living were soon hauling in hundreds of pounds of worthless sputnik grass with each lift of their dredges. Their scallop haul in 1959 amounted to a mere one percent of the previous year's crop.

"We are absolutely stunned," declared Harold F. Udell, marine biologist at the Freeport, Long Island, fisheries laboratory of the State Conservation Department. "The awesome thing about this stuff is that, unlike most marine growth, which either dies or becomes dormant in winter, it spreads profusely through the fall and winter. Control measures would be impossible." Long Island's fishermen, indeed, fear that the algae may eventually destroy all shellfish farming and fishing in their area.

Similar examples could be multiplied endlessly, for marine animals (as well as plants) are just as liable to diseases as their counterparts on land. Sometimes entire fish populations are virtually wiped out. Viruses and bacteria often cause minor and passing illnesses in fish, but these are enough to weaken the animals' resistance and make them victims of other dangers prevalent in the sea. In many cases, parasites can sterilize their hosts before they are mature or able to reproduce. Even if these fish are caught before their natural death, fungi and parasites have made them unsightly or unsavory and have thus spoiled their trade value.

Besides the ravages of disease, the survival rate of certain species of fish remains comparatively limited due to various other environmental factors. In theory, it would be possible to feed the whole of mankind from the descendants of only a few fish, since three or four female codfish, for instance, lay up to 200 million eggs. But unfortunately the mortality rate of this offspring is incredibly high. From their first day of life, hundreds of dangers threaten the existence of these eggs. Many become victims of certain fish who like to feed on them, others are killed by too much (or too little) sunlight. Comparatively few of them reach the larvae stage, and even fewer grow up to be worth catching. Of the innumerable issue of one female cod or herring, only a few finally find their way into fishermen's nets.

If ways and means could be discovered to conquer the plagues, diseases and other natural enemies of the fish world, it should be possible to reduce the mortality rate of fish larvae, similar to the ways in which we protect our sheep and cattle herds.

In their NASCO program, American oceanographers proposed the establishment of an institute for concentrated investigations of fish diseases and pests. "Intensive research in this field," they say, "should have substantial practical value. For example, although a diseased organism or a parasite is commonly limited to a single host species in one region of the world, it might infect a closely related species in another region if given the opportunity; and it would have a far more destructive effect upon the new host. Advantage could be taken of this fact by transplanting a diseased organism from one region to another to combat an undesirable species."

In practice this would mean that certain undesirable species such as starfish, rapacious molluscs and lampreys could be condemned to death if they were infected with viruses of deadly diseases. This proposal, if ever carried out after extensive studies, would certainly arouse opposition. Protests will be even stronger if some government should decide to exterminate certain larger animals which feed almost exclusively on fish, a measure that has been suggested by Japanese biologists. This would affect, for instance, large packs of seals which consume some one and a half million tons of fish annually, while millions of cormorants on the islands off Peru devour anchovies amounting to one-quarter of America's annual catch of fish.

One method of extirpating undesirable species in limited areas is proposed by Sir Alister Hardy, Linacre Professor of Zoology and Comparative Anatomy at the University of Oxford. "Fishermen of the future may be frogmen working tractor trawls sent down from parent ships above, and dragging starfish eradicators over the sea bed. . . . Eventually fishermen would pull devices over the sea floor to weed out pests that take food from more valuable fish. The pests themselves might well be converted into poultry food."

The ocean itself may point a way toward ridding its inhabitants of certain pathogenic agents. In recent years, several areas have been discovered in which diseases are almost totally unknown. All forms of life in these areas, including plants, not only achieve an old age but also astonishing sizes. One of these mysterious zones lies in the Pacific, stretching from

Panama up to the coast of Mexico. Marlins have been caught there weighing up to 2,500 pounds, while their normal weight in other areas is not more than 250 pounds. A similar disparity in size and weight has been found to exist with other species. Most Yellowtails caught off California weigh twenty pounds, while those found off Panama weigh as much as a hundred pounds. All the fish caught in this region are in excellent health. An examination of their stomachs showed no signs of the parasites or poisonous bacteria usually found in fish.

In May, 1959, an expedition from the Beaudette Foundation of Biological Research left for the waters around Central America in their ship, the *Stella Polaris*, to try to clarify this mystery of giant size and superb health. "Probably," one of the biologists stated, "there are substances in the water, perhaps brought up by northerly and southerly currents which contribute to the health of the inhabitants of the ocean. These fish do not fall ill and they live longer. Perhaps that explains their surprising size." If these substances could be identified, isolated and synthetically produced in large quantities, they could then perhaps be injected into fish ponds or future ocean farms to breed healthy fish with a longer life span.

Perhaps space satellites will be used someday to help lower the mortality rate of fish larvae. It has been observed that fewer of them grow up if the sky is very cloudy early in the year, when little sunlight—vital for the production of the phytoplankton on which the larvae feed—penetrates into the water. In such years catches were lower than normal. In the future, satellites with large reflectors could be maneuvered over likely spawning grounds should the meteorologists predict a rainy spring for such areas. Their mirrors would concentrate the sunlight to break up the pall of clouds over the fishing ground. Warmed up by the sun's rays, the water temperature could be raised sufficiently to ensure the necessary reproduction rate of plankton.

With such methods the ocean will become a giant farm where the same attention that is today given to cattle sheds will be devoted to the fishing grounds in the sea. Measures similar to those in agriculture will be taken against vermin. Finally, the breeding of young fish and the extraction of those ready for consumption will be pursued according to the latest oceanographic and marine biological knowledge.

"You don't cut down a forest with power saws and bulldozers and only then, in view of the bare stumps, start to think what to do with the area," said a Russian marine biologist. "Instead, you have the saplings ready in nurseries. Their cultivation went hand in hand with the cutting—and only the combined process can be called forestry." It will be the same with fishing. Only after the most favorable reproduction conditions have been assured for the fish population can a start be made in employing the most modern fishing methods in order to increase the annual catches. For only then can "overfishing," i.e., the dangerous decimation of certain species, be avoided. This is a vital necessity if we want to assure the future food needs of the world's increasing population.

12   Electrical Fishing

In the fall of 1959, Soviet scientists revealed plans for a number of small, fast submarines exclusively for fishing. Each vessel could hold a crew of three: captain, radio officer and "net operator." Two submarines, working in conjunction with each other, and traveling closely side by side, could, with the aid of sonar, stalk the school which had already been located from the sky by helicopters. As soon as they were near enough to the fish their paths would separate; one would hurry on to the right, the other to the left, while a big nylon net would unfold behind them. It would be fastened at the stern of each boat with special hawsers, and could enclose part of the school in a matter of minutes. When the net operators were satisfied with the way in which this unique procedure had been executed, they would give their radio officer and their captain the appropriate signal. The two boats would meet again, to surface with their booty in tow. Not far from a factory ship, the net could be anchored to buoys, and a pipe let down into the water so that the fish would be pumped up into the floating "cannery" for immediate processing. In the meantime the helicopters would have sought and located the next school and the submarines would be under way once again.

This direct fishing method, which permits the fisherman to see his prey, was conceived by a Russian professor, Lev Senkyevitch. It will afford the Russians one more way of capturing the largest hauls while Western fleets will have to do with what is left over. Such an instance occurred early in 1960 in Bering Strait, where American and Russian fishermen traditionally go after the famous king crab. The Americans had just discovered an unusually large bed, when the Russians stepped in with speedy, ultra-modern boats and snapped up the whole lot in their nets.

It need not be emphasized that Senkyevitch is developing his method with generous financial support from his government. In the Kremlin the need for more efficient new fishing methods has been recognized for a long time. If Senkyevitch had had to rely on his own initiative, submarine fishing would presumably have been retarded for years, if not decades. Unfortunately, this is the very situation facing Western engineers and oceanographers. Several up-to-date fishing methods are in the planning stage, it is true, but they are still far from being tested in the way that the Russians undertake submarine fishing tests. Different institutes receive financial aid only for much more conventional projects likely to be realized speedily in the near future. Very few interested private individuals have either the capital or creditors willing to allow them to carry their experiments through or test them to any extent. Nor can they reckon on the help and support they need from fishermen, though it is precisely the latter who stand to benefit from every new invention.

Fishing is a risky trade. No fisherman is likely to invest in expensive apparatus unless he can be certain that it will shortly return the initial outlay. If the catch in any one year is less than expected, his very existence is in peril. Fishermen have always regarded newly developed fishing methods with suspicion, as even their inventors cannot guarantee that the first attempts will produce a high catch. Most of them still prefer the same old-fashioned procedures that date back beyond their grandfathers' time. In fact, fishing equipment has improved very little over the centuries. The last innovation of any importance in the trawl, namely, the use of two boards to hold the net open, is already more than sixty years old.

Western nations will have to follow the Soviet example and put much more effort into the development of new fishing methods and apparatus, if they are to get the most from future ocean farms. At present, very few new ventures are being undertaken. In some areas of the United States, and even more so in the fishing areas of other nations, it has taken years to convince fishermen of the advantages of such devices as sonar, which today is helping them locate large shoals of fish. The Soviets, on the other hand, took action that was direct and effective, though contrary to our democratic processes: they simply ordered that sonar gear be installed on every trawler. The result was an immediate and sufficient increase in the haul per boat, which convinced the fishermen of the value of technological innovations. Today every large Russian trawler has at least one oceanographer aboard, whom the crew does not think of contemptuously as an "egghead" or "commissar." Similar cooperation between fishing and science is vital for Western fleets if they are to increase their annual catch.

Fishermen readily admit that they spend most of their time traveling and searching, rather than actually fishing. Helicopters have now come into use in America and Russia (together with light sports planes) to look for signs of big schools of fish in the sea. To detect these from helicopters, the Soviets use an instrument based on a principle derived from their submarine defense work. The new method is said to work much more quickly and reliably than the locating instrument on board many fishing vessels. As a Russian fishing expert explained, "It operates very simply and under all weather conditions. We use it in catching herring, anchovy and mackerel. A helicopter flies about fifty feet above the waves, dipping a waterproof sonar into the water. About twelve to twenty feet above the instrument there is a streamlined float which dances on the waves. This float is also connected to the helicopter by a wire, where it is attached to a fathometer. The helicopter flies ahead of the fishing fleet at a speed of 10 mph, while the co-pilot evaluates the sonar readings. If he detects a school of fish, thanks to his instruments, he can tell its depth, size and density, and also—if he has had training in marine biology— what kind of fish it is. The information is immediately communicated to the nearest fishing boat."

The great advantage of the new method is that the fish are not frightened off by the helicopter, as they are by the sound of the propellers on searching ships. In 1959 Russia began using helicopters to catch herring in the Caspian Sea. In the Barents Sea and in Far Eastern waters they are used to fish for cod and herring. Even in the Black Sea and the Sea of Azof they have been employed successfully. The haul is constantly increasing now that time is no longer wasted in fruitless searches. At the same time, naturally, care is taken that a particular fishing ground will not be "overfished."

The Russians have not only made progress in the search for fish; they are also pioneering in the application of new fishing methods. When fishermen in the Caspian Sea noticed that net fishing was proving less and less successful, they called oceanographers to their aid. On the experts' advice, they stopped using nets for certain fish and instead installed powerful floodlights on their boats to attract the schools at night. Big suction pipes then drew the fish right up into factory ships. Use of these fish dredges increased the catch fourfold.

Improved methods and apparatus have raised the total catch in other areas as well. For years fishermen from Phucc Hai in Vietnam have been fishing with hemp nets. Because of salt water rotting these had to be repaired frequently, which not only cost time and energy but also resulted in relatively modest yields. In 1957, for instance, the total catch was a mere

3,500 tons of fish. In 1958 government officials began distributing nylon nets free of charge. Although the simple Vietnamese were very suspicious of this artificial hemp, they soon had to agree that it was much more elastic and did not tear so easily. Furthermore, the new nets lasted three times as long as the old ones. Figures confirmed their impressions: in 1959 the catch had climbed to eight thousand tons and has continued to rise ever since.

The record catch achieved at Perth, Australia, in the summer of 1959 is even more impressive and was also due to the employment of modern equipment. In the six-week season over 700,000 pounds of snapper were caught. A single boat took 70,000 pounds in the space of eleven days, because, at the advice of oceanographers, weir baskets rather than fishing lines were used.

One of the chief aims of fisheries experts today is to design completely new fishing methods which will produce the greatest yield at the lowest cost. The most promising appears to be the high-seas electric fishing method developed by the German engineers, Hans Rump and Karl Heinz Ulrichs. The very first demonstrations on the open seas showed the astonishing capabilities of the system. Whereas fishermen working with nets usually have to stand exposed to icy winds and bitter cold for two hours to land a catch of a meager five tons, they can now make the same catch in five minutes by the electric method. As long as there are fish in the immediate vicinity of the boat two thousand pounds can be caught every sixty seconds. In fact, the fish swim up to be caught.

The new process works by letting down into the water an electrode which emits electrical impulses of up to 20,000 amperes. Hardly has the power been switched on before all the fish within an area of fifty to eighty feet begin a macabre dance. Without power to resist, they swim toward the electrode. This remarkable condition set up by the electric current

was called electrotaxis by the two Germans. Fish under the
spell of electrotaxis try to get as near as possible to the electrode, where the shock effects are strongest. As they do so
they are drawn into a tube by a suction pipe whose wide
mouth is immediately above the electrode. Powerful pumps
suck the fish up with a flood of water in hundreds and thousands; killed in the pipe by stronger electrical shocks, they
are washed onto the deck and transported by conveyer straight
to the processing rooms of the ship.

Fishing by electricity has been carried on for some years in
rivers and lakes, but in the open sea the physical properties of
the water have long presented additional problems. Since salt
water is a good conductor of electricity, the current spreads
very rapidly, diffusing over a wide area. As a result at a short
distance from the electrode it is already so weak that almost
no fish are attracted. Of course, it would be possible, in theory,
to send a much stronger current through the water—but that
would require generating equipment of a range of 5,000 to
7,000 kilowatts, enough to supply the power of a small town.

The German engineers solved the problem by generating a
succession of very strong electrical impulses instead of emitting a continuous flow of weaker current through the water.
The electrical impulses have the same effect as a continuous
strong current, but require a generating capacity of only 190
to 500 kilowatts.

The new application of electricity to deep-sea fishing makes
it possible to catch tremendous quantities of fish in next to no
time and with no physical effort. The electric field can be
so adjusted that only fish of a certain species or size are
caught, and then only those that are "ripe" for catching.
Young fish can be kept away from the electrode, in much the
same way as they slip through the mesh of a net. It is even
believed that the electric method yields more tasty fish, for
electrotaxis kills quickly and painlessly. Fish do not struggle

Electric deep-sea fishing will become possible thanks to a new method currently perfected by two West German engineers.

as they do in a net or on deck before they finally die, creating an accumulation of lactic acid in their muscles. Nutrition experts think that lactic acid, a product of fatigue, is detrimental to the taste and that it also causes the caught fish to decay more quickly. Fishing by electricity will soon be tried out on a large scale by experimental vessels of West Germany's and Russia's fishing fleets.

There are, of course, even more fantastic prospects for future fishermen than the "electric rod." Laurence McHugh of the American Fish and Wildlife Service predicted early in 1961 in St. Louis that some time in the future special submarines would lure fish with electronic sounds, and then literally suck them into special cargo holds within their hulls. No longer would time be wasted hunting the fish or letting out a net. Earlier we saw that certain fish react to certain sounds emitted under water. A report of the Committee on Science and Astronautics, published in 1960, said that "it would be entertaining to consider the possibility of whistling fish into range of a fishing vessel."

No doubt, most of the revolutionary fishing methods in years to come will be developed on the basis of extensive studies of fish behavior. Research by Dr. C. E. Lucas, director of Britain's Fisheries Research Laboratories in Aberdeen, Scotland, seems to indicate that fish may one day be lured into nets with the aid of chemicals. Dr. Lucas became fascinated by the fact that certain fish always return to the same place to spawn without ever losing their direction. Salmon, it has been discovered, cover hundreds, even thousands, of miles this way and many fish not only find the same river but the very same tributary where they spawned the year before. Dr. Lucas came to the conclusion that salmon literally follow their noses. As soon as they feel the spawning season approaching again, they trace certain chemical substances which have been washed out to sea by mainland rivers and then scattered by various

currents over vast areas. Certain groups of these chemical substances, Dr. Lucas believes, are characteristic of certain continental rivers and the tributaries which carried them out to
the ocean. According to the British scientist, every salmon
seems to become accustomed in its earliest weeks to the chemicals typical of its birthplace, so that years later it can track
them down in the vast ocean, although they may be so sparse
as to consist of one part chemical to a million parts of water.
The salmon finds the ocean current bringing the chemical matter from the mainland, locates the river washing it into the sea,
and follows it upstream until it reaches, finally, the tributary
which was its nursery.

Dr. Lucas' hypothesis becomes all the more interesting in
the light of the experiment made to underpin his theory. "It
is possible," he says, "to make salmon swim after an invisible
trace of a chemical substance. They presumably track it down
by means of a combined sense of smell and taste." When the
scientist stopped up the nostrils of certain salmon, the result
confirmed his expectations: the fish had much greater difficulty in following the chemical path in the water than before.
Should this discovery prove valid for other species as well, a
new fishing technique could be devised. When it is known
what chemicals different fish follow, they could be produced
synthetically and strewn in different regions. Fish encounter-
ing them would then hunt down their place of origin, where
fishermen's nets would be awaiting their arrival. Or it would
be possible to entice fish to stationary electro-dredges. Such
a method still lies far in the future. But, as Professor Senkyevitch said at the end of 1959: "One thing is certain: Fishing
will grow into a mammoth industry by the end of this century.
Improved and newly developed techniques will make it much
easier to satisfy a growing world population's skyrocketing
demand for fish."

Professor Senkyevitch envisions fish being caught on specially designated and protected fishing grounds, and prepared and packed on board modern floating factory ships during each fishing season. For the rest of the year an army of ocean farmers and technicians will see to the fertilization and preparation of the fishing grounds. Other of the sea's treasures will also be raised, for the ocean offers us not only fish but an abundance of raw materials, the disclosure and use of which are gaining in importance from day to day. To obtain seaweed, drugs and minerals from the depths, large floating islands will one day be built. Engineers in East and West are even now devoting themselves to the construction of such islands.

13

Sea Foods and Miracle Drugs

"Within a hundred years the ocean will become a serious competitor to the mainland as a supplier of raw materials," Dr. Hugh Odishaw predicted in 1958 as President of the American Committee for the International Geophysical Year. Dr. Odishaw is convinced that mankind will obtain—besides a wealth of fish—an enormous supply of other organic and inorganic matter from the world's seas. Many of his colleagues agree that industry will have to start developing the seas long before the land reserves of the world's chief raw materials have been depleted and before continental farmland becomes scarce.

In certain American states, agricultural districts already have to be protected by stringent laws from the encroachments of large cities. But how much longer will these so-called "Green Belts" be able to resist the cancerous spreading of towns and expanding industries? Today, only 3 percent of the land surface of the earth is usable for food production. Even if more land is cultivated, and even if existing farmland can be protected as Green Belts, will this guarantee that food production on the mainland can keep up with the growing world population? Turning to the sea will provide the only way out of this dilemma.

The sea is the world's largest treasure chest of food and

raw materials, of minerals and even drugs. Since 1945 about twelve million tons of food (including fish) and raw materials have been extracted from the ocean each year, representing a "harvest" of only twenty-eight pounds per square mile of water surface. This amount is only a tiny fraction of what the ocean actually has in its storehouse for the world's growing population. In the last fifteen to twenty years modern science began to recognize the importance of algae for human use and undertook a systematic study of the different kinds to be found in the waters of the world. So far, over seventeen thousand different species, of which seaweeds furnish the most familiar representatives, have been classified. Most of the important algae consist of microscopic single cells, forming phytoplankton or the "grass of the seas," as it is sometimes called.

In 1940 the Danish chemist, Professor August Krogh, found that every cubic meter of sea water contains 1.5 grams of proteins and 3.9 grams of carbohydrates in the form of plankton. This means that the Atlantic Ocean alone contains the nutritive value of twenty thousand world grain harvests. If a cheap method of obtaining and concentrating these particles were discovered, the world food problem could be solved. Eventually, experiments in this direction will have to be undertaken, but until that time we will have to concentrate on the extraction of larger algae.

Algae will one day perhaps play an even greater part in man's nutrition than fish, as they multiply at an incredible rate under favorable conditions. In 1958 a fresh-water alga was discovered in the Yellowstone National Park which reproduces a thousand times every twenty-four hours. We can estimate that there are, at present, nine times as many plants in the seas as on the mainlands. The American algologist, Dr. C. Mervin Palmer, thinks that an ocean area the size of Rhode Island, were it cultivated properly, could "produce enough algae to feed all the people on our planet."

Whereas a wheat field needs one year to bring forth a crop, algae can produce fifty crops in the same period. One acre of land normally produces less than a ton of wheat. If sugar beets are grown, a crop of as much as twenty tons per acre per year can be achieved, but in an area of water of the same size up to fifty tons of algae could be harvested every year. Plants on land need roots to stand firm in the earth and to nourish themselves. They must have strong, woody stems to withstand the wind. A great part of their energy is used up in their struggle for existence while little is left for the production of nutritious matter. Algae, on the other hand, devote all their energy to the production of nutritious substances. They have no roots, do not blossom, bear no fruit; neither do they have proper stems or leaves. Almost the whole of these water plants is composed of the same cells that comprise the leaves of land plants. Thus algae are almost 100 percent usable as opposed to only 5 or 10 percent of a land plant.

Along with land plants all algae are capable of a unique, creative, metabolic process, called photosynthesis. Utilizing sunlight they convert carbon dioxide and water into carbohydrates and oxygen. During this process, in a series of complicated steps the plant reduces carbon dioxide to sugar. After this sugar has been formed, the plants are able to convert it into starch, cellulose, sucrose, fats, proteins or oils. It is here that the capabilities of algae exceed those of terrestrial plants. A crop of soybeans, the most prolific producer of land-plant protein, yields about one ton of protein per acre per year while forty tons of seaweed, harvested on one acre, would equal a yield of twenty tons of plant protein and three tons of fat. Scientists believe that certain species of seaweed could be bred which would have a protein content of 88 percent or a fat content of 75 percent of their total weight. But even algae with a "normal" nutrient content could help to solve the world's food-shortage problem, if enough of them were cultivated.

At the San Francisco symposium of the American Public Health Association in November, 1960, Dr. William J. Oswald, associate professor of sanitary engineering and public health, said: "Computations show that five million acres of algae-animal cultures could meet the entire protein needs of the United States, whereas 300 million acres are now devoted to protein production in conventional agriculture." Dr. Oswald envisions systems in which algae grown on sewage and sea water will be fed to farm animals to produce meat, eggs, milk, wool and hides. Such algae gardens could help meet the world animal-protein deficit, which in 1960 amounted to an incredible 3,968,280,000 pounds.

Besides fat and protein, algae contain several important vitamins and a large number of chemical elements. It is these substances, which man hopes to extract, that make certain species, such as the brown and red kelp, so valuable. For centuries, indeed for millennia, seaweed washed ashore has been used by the coastal dwellers of many lands. It has been used for human consumption, as cattle fodder, fertilizer or, especially in eastern Asia, to obtain certain curing potions. Recently even such unlikely products as alcohol and gasoline have been made from seaweed. (Here we are reminded of Glauco Partel's prediction that plankton will be used for fuel in submarines.)

Off the Norwegian coast, brown kelp is already being cultivated on a larger scale than anywhere else in the world. This particular offshore region is especially fertile because every spring the melting snows wash certain minerals from the mountains into the sea. Additional nutritive substances are borne along by the Gulf Stream, thus creating a natural sea farm in the area. Under the watchful care of the official governmental authorities, the seaweed forests are harvested several times a year. Before the war Norway used to produce 67,000 tons of brown-kelp meal annually in this way.

Norwegian kelp meal is used not only for fertilizer and

animal food but also for human consumption. In Scandinavia and Germany it is possible to buy bread containing 2 to 10 percent kelp meal besides wheat. A slice of this bread tastes like plain cake. The German food chemist, Heinrich Lienau, introduced "alga bread" as early as 1938, when he opened a factory near Reykjavik, Iceland, in which he baked bread from seaweed meal for the first time.

Lienau's bread is neither green nor moldy-smelling, for it is not baked with washed-up, decaying seaweed but with the flour obtained from fresh algae harvested on Norway's sea farms. A further point in its favor, besides its low cost and ready availability, is that the bread keeps fresh for weeks. Alga bread may well be the bread of the future, as it contains not only numerous vitamins, but also all the other important ingredients of brown kelp, such as fats and proteins.

The high nutritive value of algae was clearly proven by experiments in this country with algin, an extract of brown kelp. Produced by the Algin Kelp Meal Company in Chicago, it is used by an increasing number of farmers as fertilizer or fodder. According to the firm's figures, the meal contains 5.7 percent proteins, 2.6 percent fats, 58.6 percent nitrogen-free substances, 10.7 percent moisture, 15.4 percent potassium and twelve different vitamins, including A, B_1, B_2, B_{12} and C. There are twenty-one hormone and protein bodies, but most important, the mineral and nonmineral elements number over sixty, from silver and gold to aluminum, sulphur, zinc and tungsten. Because of its high mineral content, the meal has proved successful in building up undernourished animals. It also seems effective in preventing animal diseases such as hoof-and-mouth, in reducing the death rate, and in increasing the size of chicken eggs and other animal offspring. On a mink-breeding establishment, 1 percent of the meal was mixed with the normal food; it was found that in five months up to 9 percent of the standard food could be saved. Although the minks had less to eat in bulk, they thrived more than ever; they grew at a faster rate, their skins were more lustrous and brought a higher market price.

Some scientists now believe that in fifteen years algin meal will become the chief animal fodder, as well as a fertilizer. As soon as cattle can successfully change over to nutritious marine plants, part of the world's pastures can be tilled for additional agricultural space.

The Japanese are among the leaders in algae cultivation. One of their chemists, Dr. Hiroshi Tamiya, has for years entertained his guests at meals in which the bread, cakes and ice cream have all been made from the same substance: seaweed. Many Japanese shops sell sweets made of seaweed, and at weekly markets one can find plankton cubes, which, when boiled in water, provide a soup which is said to be very tasty. Hundreds of different kinds of seaweed grow in the waters surrounding Japan's island empire; many boats find it more profitable to concentrate on the seaweed catch rather than toil for fish. Hundreds of thousands of tons of algae are brought ashore annually, and in many districts a distinct seaweed industry is building up. Today seaweed is being made into a toothpaste which does not dry up if the cap of the tube is lost. Inks, jellies, soaps, explosives, dyes, welding materials, medicines and cosmetics are also being manufactured from seaweed.

To Western palates, seaweed dishes will undoubtedly taste flat and flavorless. But this difficulty will be overcome when American scientists succeed in isolating the flavor enzymes of beefsteaks and pork chops which give these expensive meats their specific taste. The flavor could then be produced artificially, so that cooked seaweed could be made to taste like steak or chops. "Before the year 2057 we shall be eating steaks composed of extracted alga-protein, spiced with enzymes and made chewable by suitable digestible plastic," explained the American biologist, James Bonner.

Modern food chemistry will ensure that marine plants find their way increasingly into Western kitchens in future decades, and the psychological tactics of modern advertising will certainly have to be used with full force. Most European and U.S. housewives cannot imagine living on algae because they have never been exposed to the idea of its eventual necessity. If algae are appetizingly packed and properly flavored, housewives may come to accept them. Besides being cheaper than pork or beef, seaweed dishes will be actually more nourishing.

There are already plans to build alga factories in the shallow bays of those countries whose populations suffer from undernourishment and lack of protein. Large sun reflectors would warm the sea to speed up the reproduction of marine plants. These factories could gradually be converted to complete automation, robots undertaking the harvest and the processing of seaweed into its diverse products. The United States government has also called upon all inventors to develop an economical method of harvesting algae in fresh-water lakes, and eventually in salt-water areas.

The Russians have a fairly accurate idea of how to proceed with the harvesting of extensive maritime "soil." Professor Senkyevitch is sure that "the new science of submarine agronomy will be with us by the year 2000." Soviet marine agronomists would like to turn the Barents Sea, the Sea of Azov and the northwest corner of the Black Sea into seaweed-cultivation areas. At a conference Professor Senkyevitch reported that "Sea farmers will harvest down to a depth of three hundred feet in diving vessels assisted by remote control harvesters to obtain useful plants in these marine meadows, or fish out growing seaweed forests."

In recent years the sea has also become the source of many substances used in chemistry and medicine, and there has been a growing emphasis on marine biological research aimed at discovering new medicaments and remedies. Up to 1945 the Japanese were the only people to obtain the gelatin-like sub-

stance agar-agar from red algae. Since the end of World War
II America, South Africa, Australia and Russia have joined
them. Agar-agar can be used as a culture medium for bacteria,
as a medicine and also as a household gelatin.

Some kinds of brown algae contain up to 0.4 percent iodine
and for a long time were the only source of this important
chemical element. They were dried, burned and the residue
treated in a special chemical process. Nowadays iodine is also
found on the mainland—in certain deposits of prehistoric seas,
such as in the high deserts of Chile. Bromine, on the other
hand, is now exclusively extracted from the ocean, which contains 99 percent of the world's stocks. On many coasts, especially American, factories have been erected to obtain bromine
from the sea as it becomes increasingly more important in the
production of gasoline, dyes, fire-extinguishing fluids and
photographic chemicals. It is also indispensable in the manufacture of chemical warfare substances and sedatives.

Another remedy, milk of magnesia, comes from the mineral
magnesia extracted from the sea water in enormous quantities.
Vitamin D has been derived from the sea for many years in
the form of cod liver oil. In fact, sea water itself, taken in small
quantities, is known to kill many forms of staphylococcus.

The chemical and pharmaceutical industry is now beginning
to rely more and more on the ocean as a source for new
"miracle drugs." Whereas during the first half of this century
scientific expeditions were undertaken in jungles and back-
woods to investigate the medical cures, herbs and plants used
by the witch doctors of primitive tribes, similar expeditions
will now be led by chemists in diving vessels and diving suits
to discover new drugs among the animal and plant life of the
ocean's forests.

An American toxicologist, Dr. Bruce Halstead, declared
toward the end of 1959: "Scientific proof is mounting up to
show that harmful marine creatures and their poisons are the

starting point for life-giving antibiotics, cancer preventatives and other important drugs." Dr. Ross F. Nigrelli, director of the Laboratory of Marine Biochemistry and Ecology, Brooklyn, New York, explained at about the same time: "I believe that modern chemistry will be taking a far greater number of antibiotics with far greater effectiveness from the ocean than have ever been discovered on our continents before," and in a 1960 report of the American Medical Association it is stated that "the sea may be an untapped reservoir of answers to scores of medical problems."

Fish poisons, for instance, which have previously caused sudden death, will in the future be used to prevent these deaths. Since the beginning of 1959 American ichthyologists have been examining the possible curative effect of the poison of some three hundred fish and marine invertebrates throughout the world's seas. As a result of their work, there is now hope that a certain growth-inhibiting substance in the strong poison of the sea cucumber may one day be used in the fight against cancer. Called holothurin, this poison affects the nerves considerably more than digitalis, a poison derived from the foxglove plant and, in a diluted form, often prescribed as medicine. Holothurin even cleans clothing better than soap.

In his laboratory in the Aquarium on Coney Island, Dr. Nigrelli had some cancerous tissues grafted into mice, and allowed them forty-eight hours to take root and spread. This particular form of cancer he chose usually proves fatal to mice within ten to twelve days. Forty-eight hours after the start of the experiment Dr. Nigrelli injected a dilute solution of holothurin directly into the diseased tissues, with the effect that the poison slowed down or even totally halted tumor growth.

Dr. Halstead, who founded a research institute on the California coast in which he could study fish poisons, is pursuing similar experiments. The trigger fish is said to have a substance in its poison that affects certain components in the blood, while the poison of the toad fish may one day be used to combat diabetes. Halstead is devoting special attention to those poisonous fish whose organs contain matter that is known as the second strongest poison. (Botulinus bacteria, which cause food poisoning, are the strongest of all poisons.) Various Japanese doctors, Halstead reported at a conference, have for decades been obtaining from this poison a remedy to relieve the torturing pain of cancer patients, although it was unable to stop their death. It is now hoped that this path can be pursued further with success.

Only recently was it realized that liver oil from cod and certain other fish seems to reduce the cholesterol content in the human body, in contrast to the effects of other animal fats. This might be helpful in preventing heart disease. It has also been found that the tiny eggs of sea urchins are an ideal medium for testing the effects of various chemicals in halting mitosis, or cell division. And Dr. Dixy Lee Ray, consultant in biological oceanography to the National Science Foundation, declared in 1960, "An effective antiviral agent has been found in the muscles of abalone."

Dr. John C. Houck of the Biochemical Research Laboratory of the Children's Hospital in Washington believes that an extract from a particular sort of seaweed can deter the development of stomach ulcers. Moreover, one kind of sea sponge from the North American Atlantic Coast contains ectyonin, a substance which has turned out especially effective in overcoming certain bacteria. Success was achieved with it not merely in the test tube but also in "guinea pigs." Dr. Nigrelli, who was in charge of the work, had fish injected with purulent bacteria, which killed them immediately. Other fish that were inoculated simultaneously with a solution of ectyonin survived the test.

In Japan a gelatin-like extract of brown algae has lately

found a new application in operations as a substitute for blood plasma. Called alginon, it consists of large protein molecules. Solutions prepared from it remain in the arteries like natural blood plasma and stop the blood pressure from falling to a dangerous level during surgical operations. Dr. Sannomiya Masanobu of Kyushu University, Fukuoka, has used alginon successfully in over a hundred abdominal operations. In experiments on animals whose inner organs had been severely burnt no harm was noticeable after a transfusion with the new "algae plasma." After less than twenty-four hours 70 percent of the alginon had been excreted, so that there is no danger of its being secreted in the body.

It is possible that man will one day make use of some of the remarkable properties of other algae and invertebrate marine creatures. Certain of these organisms excrete substances that repel one form of life while attracting another. It is hoped that a careful examination of the biochemical properties of these substances will result in fresh products like insecticides, weed killers, fertilizers, medicaments and antibiotics.

The expedition of the Beaudette Foundation to investigate the enormous growth of marlins and yellowtails off Panama, and the reason why they do not fall ill, will at the same time study why the algae in that area attain a length of several hundred yards and have "trunks" with a diameter of over three feet. Since the summer of 1959 scientists have been filtering samples of water to obtain even the tiniest organisms contained therein. These too will be studied for their antibiotic and biochemical properties.

Just as the fertilization of a trout nursery has proved to be effective, so the extraction of raw materials and drugs from the sea will one day be intensified in a similar way. Experts are already seriously considering where and to what extent this extraction should take place. Some think that the best method would be artificial islands constructed in certain ocean areas such as the Sargasso Sea. Large pontoons would be made of hollow concrete slabs close to the coast, or they might be constructed of more modern materials such as plastics. They would then be towed out to the open sea, where they would be joined up to form large circles, anchored to underwater mountains or fitted with large propellers so that they could change their position at will.

The inside of every such artificial atoll would then form a kind of harbor protected from wind and weather where the work could proceed. Factories would be built on the pontoons themselves to process the raw materials obtained from the sea. Workmen's accommodations, mostly under the surface of the waves, would extend deep into the water from the bottom of the pontoons. Sufficient light could reach the lowest rooms through transparent plastic walls.

Fibers and synthetic leathers, made from plankton and fish protein, would serve as clothing for the inhabitants of the islands as well as exports to the continents. These products are quite feasible. In World War II the Germans made soles for shoes from the strong skins of sting rays, while shark skin also served as a leather substitute. Even so-called "fish suits," whose fibers had been spun from the protein of fish (mainly herring), were on sale.

In his book *How Will We Live?* Dr. Walter Greiling suggests other possibilities for the use of the ocean's raw materials:

> Small chemical factories processing protein into synthetic materials and fibers, extracting paper from bleached seaweed, melting glass in oil-heated furnaces and producing ceramics can work on the sea itself. The oil for heating can be taken from the plankton, just as the fuel for aircraft and diesel oil for fishing vessels. Deep-sea clay, sand and chalk for

the ceramic and building industries will be raised from the sea floor by dredges or scraped off the peaks of underwater elevations. Really the only things that need be got from the mainland are iron and steel, other heavy metals and the great amount of cement. Light metals can be extracted from the sea water. Many chemicals are given off in the process as by-products.

Some of these raw materials, according to Dr. Greiling, could even be turned into furniture, wall panels and many kinds of household appliances. Poured into special dies, they would be lowered deep into the sea, where the enormous pressure would act like a hydraulic press, compressing the raw ingot material to the desired shape.

14　　Mining the Ocean Floor

For decades oceanographers have known that far greater quantities of every kind of metal exist in the 335 million cubic miles of ocean water than are to be found in all the earth's mines put together. But they are spread through the ocean in the form of very fine particles (called ions) and it would be a difficult and costly venture to extract them in large quantities at this time. In 1958, however, it was discovered that vast areas of the ocean floor are carpeted with concretions of various metals in nodules of fist size and larger. Although the first samples were found eighty-five years before the International Geophysical Year, their importance remained undetected. Toward the end of the last century, the British *Challenger* and later the U.S. *Albatross* had fished up some of these peculiar crumbling nodules. Chemical analysis proved that they contained large amounts of iron and manganese.

In the years following this discovery, though there were innumerable speculations as to the origin of these nodules, no one seemed to consider the possibility of raising them to the surface for eventual commercial use. The supply of metal on the continents appeared to be sufficient for some time to come, and even if the resources of the sea had been required, the necessary technical apparatus to raise them off the ocean floor was not available. Had the matter been followed up more thoroughly, someone might have discovered what was proved as late as 1958 by oceanographers of the University of California: that large areas of the world's deep-sea floor are literally studded with these brown-black nodules. Most of those near the continents' coastlines are no larger than ping-pong balls. Further out in the ocean, however, where the water reaches a depth of fourteen thousand feet or more, they may measure up to two feet in diameter.

Dr. Roger Revelle believes that these metal concretions are the product of electrochemical deposits over the course of thousands of years. Dr. John W. Graham of the Woods Hole Oceanographic Institution holds another view. "The metal balls were produced by living organisms," he says. "They contain the tiny shell of a foraminifera, a one-cell organism, right in the center. When this died an even smaller organism, as yet unidentified, settled on the outer wall of the foraminifer shell, attracted by the latter's protein content. The new organism . . . used sea water for food. It derived valuable metals from it and concentrated them in and around itself. It was a natural mine! That is why the nodules are so full of mineral substances."

An analysis of the spherical metal hoards in 1958 revealed an amazing phenomenon. Dr. Edward D. Goldberg of the Scripps Institution of Oceanography established that the average metal content of numerous samples collected from widely differing regions amounted to 20 percent manganese, 15 percent iron and 0.5 percent nickel, cobalt and copper respectively. This was only the average content. In some regions the metal ratio was considerably higher. John L. Mero, research engineer for the University of California Department of Mineral Technology, reports that there are nodules containing up to 45 percent manganese, 1 percent cobalt, 1.4 percent nickel and 1.8 percent copper, as well as smaller ratios of rare earths, vanadium, molybdenum and other metals. The majority of these nodules are believed to lie at a depth of ten thousand feet or more; occasionally, however, they have been found in shallow regions where the ocean floor is less than four thousand feet deep.

Two questions that naturally arose for experts were: how many of these nodules are there altogether, and how can they best and most easily be obtained? Widespread prospecting samples from the different oceans indicate that the nodules cover extensive areas of the Pacific, Atlantic and Indian ocean floors. How concentrated they are at individual spots has been determined in only a few places where photographs were taken of the sea floor. In all these cases, it was found that a quarter to a half of the sea bed was littered with metallic nodules. Detailed information about the density of the various concentrations on the ocean floor will be provided by the research diving boats of coming decades. Scientists of NASCO already believe that "the total reserves of metals on the bed of the world's seas appear to be extraordinarily large." Optimists talk in terms of 500 to 1,000 billion tons.

Mero made more cautious estimates in 1959. According to him, the nodules worth lifting to the surface are distributed over about 22 million square miles of the ocean floor. The quantity in the Atlantic amounts to 45 billion tons; there are 41.4 billion tons on the floor of the Indian Ocean, and in the Pacific stocks covering an area larger than the whole of Africa amount to 112 billion tons. In other words, a total of 198 billion tons of metal-rich nodules could be raised from the ocean floor. Mero goes on to say that at 1958 prices the gross value of metal derived from every ton raised from the bottom would be about ten dollars. "That means a wealth of $340,000 is waiting to be salvaged along every square mile of the ocean floor. In the Southern Pacific, where the metallic content of the nuggets is particularly great, the value per square mile [of sea floor] rises to $10 million."

In March of 1959 certain salvaging and mining experts discussed the feasibility of extracting the metal resources of the sea floor at a conference of the Mining Institute in San Francisco. Shareholders of mining companies were the most vocal in urging that this question be added to the agenda. The experts outlined the various solutions to the technical problems involved, all of which demanded an enormous initial investment. Some of these experts even doubted whether it would be profitable to obtain ores from the sea. A representative of the largest manganese processing firm in the U.S., for instance, maintained that "as long as the price of manganese imported from Brazil, Africa and India does not rise by more than 50 percent, we shall not be interested in manganese from the ocean floor." William Dorrence, Assistant Director of Scientific Research at the General Dynamics Corporation, added that "it is still easier and cheaper to prepare mainland ores of low manganese content." Yet most of his colleagues admitted that one day we might have to make use of the ocean's ore deposits.

It would be most unwise to let that day arrive without having made the appropriate preparations. Fully realizing this, America's oceanographers in their NASCO report have requested the sum of $2.6 million to carry out the necessary studies to discover whether and how it will be possible to make use of the ores on the sea floor. At this writing, their efforts have remained unsuccessful, and the consequences of neglect of this important area of research were impressively outlined by Mero early in 1960:

"It seems strange that the U.S. Government will invest hundreds of millions of dollars to develop ore deposits in places such as Cuba—only to lose the entire investment—but cannot spend a few hundred thousand over the years to help develop the vastly greater in size and richer in grade deposits on the ocean floor. In addition to being politically free, these deposits would be royalty-free ores for us.

"We obtain the bulk of our manganese and cobalt from foreign sources which are sometimes politically unstable. Some of the countries from which we obtain metals contained in the sea floor ores seem to be politically stable. However, as these countries industrialize, they will tend to consume their minerals themselves and try to sell to the United States manufactured products rather than the raw materials. This is already happening in the case of India and South Africa, which are forcing us to take an increasing amount of ferromanganese rather than the manganese ore itself."

The Russians, on the other hand, fully realize the importance of free maritime ore deposits, and make efforts to chart their locations, which extend to right under the Americans' noses. Senator Magnuson maintains that Soviet scientists have gone as far as to take "clear, distinct photographs of the nodules three hundred miles off the coast of Southern California," while Russia's Professor Tscherbakov predicted at the end of 1959 that "the Soviet Union will soon move into all areas of the open sea to study possibilities of ore extraction."

Obviously, the United States should develop suitable deep-sea mining methods as soon as possible, without even waiting for the first Russian "ocean-floor mine." Mero has for some time been studying the possibility of recovering the nodules. One of his suggestions involves a flotilla of metal dredges that would be dragged over the bottom to scrape off the nodules, in the same manner as research ships now bring up samples of the sea floor. This process has one disadvantage: much time is wasted while the dredges are lowered and hauled up again. It might be more profitable to employ large suction pipes for this purpose. Such apparatus, a kind of "underwater vacuum cleaner," has long been installed in shallow waters to suck up the deposits on the bottom of lakes, harbors and rivers. If powerful pumps could be fitted to the suction pipes, Mero believes, there is no reason why work could not be undertaken at depths of thirteen thousand feet.

In the distant future, the most economical way of extracting the nodules would involve diving boats, though this would mean a considerable initial investment. Grapplers or scoops, attached to submarine vessels, could be used at different depths. The nodules could then be picked up on the bottom, free from mud or sediment, and reloaded onto the attached deep-sea barges. Only the technicians' gondola of this barge train would need to be strong enough to withstand the water pressure; the hold of the other barges could be made of lighter-weight materials, such as sheets of aluminum. Once filled with the mineral nodules, the loaded barge would surface as an empty one submerged. The full hold could be uncoupled at the surface, to be towed by freight helicopter straight to the shore or to an ore ship in the immediate vicinity. An empty hold could then be attached to the gondola for a new descent to the ocean floor.

This method has several great advantages. The surface of the ocean floor would not be ravaged by dredges or suction pipes. Moreover, by employing diving bells, oceanographers would be able to make a simultaneous investigation of the ocean floor, since practically every square inch would have to be covered in the course of the work. But this more complicated method probably will not be used for some time, as dredges and suction pipes are ready at hand and have been tried and proved successful. "Modern techniques," said Mero late in 1959, "have already progressed so far that there are no longer any insuperable difficulties connected with rescuing the sea's ores."

With the necessary financial backing maritime mining should prove profitable within a few years of embarking on a project. Mero believes that working by the suction method ought to cost about two dollars per ton of ore, a small sum to which transport costs, varying from a dollar and a half to eight dollars, according to the distance to the furnaces, would have to be added. With a reasonable amount of investment, more con-

ventional methods (such as dredging) could be improved to
permit the daily raising of five thousand tons of the hoard to
the surface. If this haul contained an average amount of metal,
and if 80 to 90 percent of the metal could be extracted, such a
process would represent an annual manganese production of
288,000 tons, or one-quarter of America's requirements in
1959. In addition, the by-products of nickel, cobalt, and copper would amount to several thousand tons annually. The total
hoard on the bottom, Mero estimates, is forty billion tons of
manganese and a billion tons of nickel, copper and cobalt respectively. These stocks on the ocean floor could cover the
United States' requirements for several hundred years to come.

Mero anticipates that the first attempts at mining will be
undertaken in 1965, either by a group of industrial concerns
or within the framework of a program at governmental level.

Dr. Revelle of the Scripps Institution of Oceanography is
just as confident. "One day manganese will be harvested like
fish. It is present in the sea in such quantities that only as
much as can be sold will be extracted." The same applies to
the other metals and minerals contained in the ocean. The
rich phosphate deposits off the California coast, for instance,
amounting to about 100 million tons, could be raised at a cost
of a mere three dollars per ton. It has been known since 1940
that this material, highly important in the production of fertilizers, covers the ocean floor in the form of nodules up to three
feet in diameter, amounting in some areas to as much as thirty
pounds per square foot of ocean floor. Yet California is still
importing 150,000 tons of crude phosphate annually at a cost
of twelve dollars per ton for the nation's farms. Half of this
sum is spent on transport, which would obviously be eliminated if the deposits forty miles off the coast could be salvaged.

A far richer mineral treasure house than the sea floor, however, is the sea water itself. It contains, in solution, all identi-

fied natural elements, forty of them in measurable amounts.
The quantities of sodium and chlorine, combined as the salt we
use to season our food, are literally inexhaustible. The total can
be estimated at fifty quadrillion tons. Spread evenly over the
whole surface of the earth, every mountain and valley, every
sea and island would be covered by a salt crust 450 feet thick.

Next to the vast amounts of sodium and chlorine, the quantities of calcium, potassium, sulphur, magnesium and bromine
contained in sea water are so significant that special attention
has for a long time been devoted to their extraction.

Magnesium, which for many years was obtained by processing dolomite, a common mainland mineral, has been in increasing demand for industrial purposes since the beginning of the
Second World War, as have all the above-named minerals.
When magnesium became essential in the aircraft industry as
well as in the munitions factories during World War II,
America turned to the processing of sea water in order to extract the mineral in ever-increasing quantities. Every cubic
mile of ocean water contains over four million tons of magnesium.

Most other elements, however, amount to only a few milli-
grams per ten cubic feet of sea water, which is not significant
enough to justify mass extraction with presently available
methods—even though the total amount of these metals contained in the vast water masses of the ocean is impressive. The
world's seas, for example, contain more silver than the mines
of all the continents combined; the same is true of gold. Sea
water contains enough uranium to provide man with atomic
energy for decades to come, while quantities of radium exist
in greater concentration in the sediments of the ocean floor
than in the radioactive rocks of the Belgian Congo.

To obtain these and other elements from the sea in reasonable amounts, vast quantities of sea water would have to be
processed, an exorbitantly expensive undertaking by conven-

tional methods. In 1959, however, the Armour Company of Chicago applied for a patent of a process whereby even these widely dispersed elements could be extracted from sea water at relatively low costs. Developed by Professor Sebba of the Witwatersrand University in Johannesburg, it could yield six hundred tons of aluminum, two tons of uranium and twenty ounces of gold per day from the sea. The so-called "flotation process" would work roughly like this: A certain area in the sea would be closed off and a few dozen pipes laid on the bottom with fine holes drilled in their upper sides. A special lather would be pumped through the pipes, varying with the metal to be obtained, and ejected from the pipes in the form of tiny bubbles. Rising to the surface, the bubbles would "tear" minute particles of metal out of the water and carry them to the surface. Enclosed in the foam created by the millions of rising bubbles, these particles could then be scooped off by special devices. What is characteristic of Professor Sebba's method is the fact that certain lathers attract certain elements in the water. Bubbles from caustic lye, for instance, would attract only cobalt, leaving a green, cobalt-containing foam on the surface. With such a method, numerous metals could be obtained from the sea at relatively low cost, including those metals that have so far remained beyond our reach.

In his book *How Will We Live?* Walter Greiling assumes that man will one day also make use of marine plants and creatures to obtain metals from the sea. Nylon nets could surround a submarine garden, "in which specially cultivated types of seaweed would draw rare metals from the sea water and store them in their cell structure," as all animals and plants do to a small extent.

> This seaweed would be harvested, dried and carefully burnt, so that the metals, iodine and many

chemicals could be separated from the ashes. . . .
Even certain fishes' intestines are enriched by various
metals. These fish could be colonized in underwater
gardens and fed with the plankton passing overhead.
In order to increase the amount of metal derived in
this way by as much as a few grams per pound, the
fish could be exposed to radioactive rays, so that
their offspring would produce even more metal!

Oysters store more copper in their cell structure than is to
be found in the sea water surrounding them, but even today
we do not know how they do it. "However, when we find
out," said chemist Clifford C. Furnas of Buffalo University, "we
shall be in a position to obtain the almost unlimited mineral resources of the sea cheaply."

One of the most peculiar and uncanny suggestions that may
one day be employed in the extraction of raw materials from
the sea originated in the mind of John von Neumann, one of
the world's great mathematicians. If this project ever ma-
terializes, beachcombers of the future may encounter hundreds and thousands of whale-like creatures littering the shores
in the autumn of every year. They will not be fish, however,
but machines, robots built by robots, all identical right down
to the last bolt. They will be made from raw materials
derived exclusively from the sea and will be the "progeny" of
a single robot made by man's hand, which originally had been
put into the sea with the purpose of reproducing itself.

Admittedly, this idea sounds a bit farfetched and maybe it
will never be realized entirely, but nevertheless it is interesting
to note. Von Neumann, who developed the electronic computers ENIAC and MANIAC, believed that it would eventually be possible to construct a robot capable of reproducing
itself, and not only once but continually, so that it would
"bear" quite a number of children, which in turn would pro-

create ad infinitum. From this original robot, reproducing in geometric progression, it would not take long for hundreds and even thousands or tens of thousands of identical machines to come into being. Two conditions would be necessary for this theory to be realized in practice: a continuous supply of energy to maintain production, and sufficient raw materials to construct the different parts.

The ocean stores enough raw materials for the realization of this plan. The original robot would start by making the separate parts, such as wires, spools, synthetic materials, coatings of magnesium and aluminum plates. It would fit them together and provide its creation with an exact copy of its assembly program so that it in turn could begin work on a new robot immediately.

At the same time all the "artificial fish" would derive the necessary energy from the sun by means of special solar cells and batteries, similar to the ones used today to power the equipment on board many of our artificial earth satellites.

The lives of many of these robots would undoubtedly be ended prematurely due to mechanical failures, but it seems feasible that a proportion would increase sufficiently to ensure that a gigantic army of them would eventually populate the sea like an enormous shoal of metal fish!

The "harvest" would occur once or twice a year. A certain number of robots could be attracted to land by means of radio signals, but in not too great a quantity, otherwise the total number would suffer. On the shore they would be loaded onto trucks by electric cranes and brought to the "slaughterhouse," where other robots would dismember them and send them on to the smelting stations.

Serious discussions have been held to discover whether such a program would be practicable and worthwhile. The American physicist, Edward F. Moore, who has been particularly occupied with this question, is convinced that all the technical problems could be solved, and estimates the time necessary at between five and ten years, if the world's best scientists would cooperate on the task. The expenses would run to between $45 million and $78 million. A relatively primitive robot capable of reproducing itself has already been built at New York University. Engineers had, however, to supply it with ready-made parts, while it obtained its energy from house current.

Even if the sea's metals will not be extracted by "child-bearing" robots for a long time to come, some of the other methods mentioned will undoubtedly be in use before the end of our century.

All these considerations point to a new and serious problem on the horizon, which deals with who has the right to extract the ocean's mineral resources. At the present time, no nation can claim them because the high seas are international and neutral. "But in the day of bottom crawlers," it is said in a report on *Ocean Sciences and National Security* by the Committee on Science and Astronautics, "perhaps two competing nations equally interested in mining a supply of manganese nodules in 12,000 feet of water, 500 miles from the nearest land, will come armed with the counterpart of the weapons of the gold prospector." The taking will then be on the basis of "first come, first served," unless new international laws can be drawn up which will regulate the just distribution of all ocean riches from top to bottom. The arguments over fishing, though still comparatively harmless, prove the necessity for such laws, for as the conquest and exploitation of the sea proceed, far graver social, economic and, above all, international, legal and political problems will ensue, for which we cannot yet foresee solutions.

An incident of this nature occurred in mid-January of 1960, when the Russians declared an area of about 10,000 square miles in the Pacific to be a testing area for one of their intercontinental ballistic missile experiments. The reaction in

America to this step ranged from open revolt to perplexity. Senator Mike Mansfield, known for his aggressiveness, demanded that "the State Department should protest strongly." Former President Truman spoke of a "provocative act," and other political personalities expressed their annoyance at this snatching of part of the "American Ocean," as the Pacific is often called. By their action the Russians had merely appropriated a right which the other great powers had previously adopted time and time again. The United States had autocratically declared an area of 400,000 square miles of open sea to be a "danger zone" early in 1954. They carried out their final preparations for the hydrogen bomb there.

In May, 1957, Great Britain arbitrarily termed an area of the open sea "dangerous water" and she as good as fenced off 350 square miles in the vicinity of Christmas Island to test her atomic bombs.

All these actions were gross infringements of the traditional concept of the Freedom of the Sea, according to which all nations in peacetime have an equal right to the use of the sea. In 1926 the International Law Society strengthened this concept by stating that no nation "could claim any part of the open sea or erect any obstacles therein which might limit the full and free use of the same." The fact that limitations have been imposed by all great powers, and that more and more will be imposed now that the exploitation of the sea has begun, is a sign that the concept of the freedom of the sea is obsolete.

This concept came about because the sea's most important feature once was that it provided a cheap, world-wide route for traffic. "I am afraid that the idea of the freedom of the seas is somewhat incompatible with their efficient and wise exploitation," declared the American oceanographer, Columbus O'D. Iselin, late in 1959. "The economic and social problems that will be encountered as we begin seriously to exploit marine resources seem to me to be formidable, much more formidable than the remaining unsolved scientific problems. Some very wise agency needs to be developing the ground rules within which the vast marine resources can be developed in an efficient and safe manner for the benefit of all mankind."

Iselin seemed to find justification of his statement at the United Nations Conference on the Law of the Sea which took place at Geneva in March, 1960, after two years' preparations. The conference lasted six weeks and closed having achieved virtually nothing. It had been the intention of some representatives, led by the Canadian and American delegations, to extend the traditional limits of sovereign waters from three miles (the range of the old coastal batteries) to six miles. Russia, the countries of the Eastern block, together with Iceland and most South American and Middle East states were for an extension to twelve miles. In the ensuing vote, the U.S. proposal failed to get the necessary two-thirds majority by a single vote. The result: a hopeless confusion in maritime law, for even the Russian suggestion found no audience. The three-mile limit was upheld, despite the fact that many nations no longer respect it.

In the course of the next few years, new conferences will be called to settle these complicated legal questions, for one day all claims to ownership of the sea will have to be cleared up with regulations on the stocks of ores on the ocean floor as well as on the seaweed and shoals of fish existing in what is still today a free and open sea.

15 A Million Years of Energy

"Getting water, quite ordinary drinking water, will be America's number one problem in a few years," predicted Dr. A. L. Miller of the Office of Saline Water late in 1959, while almost simultaneously delegates at a mining congress in New York reached the unanimous conclusion that man's supply of energy from such traditional fuel sources as crude oil, wood and coal is running low. Yet both drinking water and fuel exist in greater quantities in the oceans of the world than man will ever require in the foreseeable future.

Every pint of sea water could be drunk if the salt were extracted, or could provide enough fuel to generate 1,500 kilowatt hours of electricity, as much as a family of four consumes in a whole year.

It is relatively simple to extract the salt from sea water, but generally quite expensive. Obtaining fuel from sea water on the other hand is a hundred times cheaper than the most economical methods of mining hard coal. A controlled release of this fuel's latent energy, however, is "one of the most difficult, but also one of the most important and challenging tasks that has ever been attempted," according to Dr. Amasa S. Bishop, an American nuclear research scientist.

The mysterious fuel contained in the sea is none other than an isotope of hydrogen, known as deuterium or heavy hydrogen. It was discovered in 1932 by the American chemist, Harold C. Urey, and his associates, but at that time nobody realized the importance it would have in the coming atomic age. Urey found that one part of heavy hydrogen is represented in every six thousand parts of sea water. What this amounts to on an oceanic scale was summed up by Lewis L. Strauss, the former chairman of the American Atomic Energy Commission:

"It is estimated that there is enough deuterium in the sea to generate a thousand times more energy for the next million years than is generated in the whole world today."

Since 1945 nuclear scientists in Russia, the United States, Great Britain and other countries have been occupied with trying to bring about a *controlled* thermonuclear reaction in which cheap deuterium would be the main source of energy.

This process, which can be compared to a very slow hydrogen bomb explosion, calls for the generation of temperatures in the range of 100,000,000 degrees Centigrade. At this tremendous heat, the nuclei of deuterium atoms are under such pressure that they are able to fuse into helium nuclei. (It is precisely from this same nuclear fusion that the sun and the countless stars of the universe derive their energy. In the case of the sun, for instance, 50,000 million tons of water per day are reduced to helium.)

The high temperatures necessary to "ignite" a thermonuclear reaction account for the most difficult problems in creating an "artificial sun" here on earth. Not only are they difficult to produce, but there is no building material which can withstand a temperature of more than a few thousand degrees. An H-reactor built from conventional metals would melt like butter. One solution seems to be the creation of strong magnetic fields which will keep the hot deuterium gas, or plasma as it is called, away from the material walls of the H-reactor.

Extremely high temperatures such as are necessary for a

nuclear fusion have already been maintained for fractions of a second. And early in 1961 the Atomic Energy Commission hopefully announced that its scientists appeared to be coming closer to the long-sought goal of igniting the first controlled thermonuclear reaction. Were the ignition to be achieved—in which a device called Toy Top III is used—the way for step two would be prepared: development of a thermonuclear reactor for the conversion of the ocean's heavy hydrogen into an almost inexhaustible supply of energy.

In 1959 the English Nobel Prize winner, Sir George Thomson, predicted "that in about fifteen years' time a working H-reactor" would be built. American experts share his confidence. In 1960, Edward W. Harold of the Radio Corporation of America compared the "advances of work on controlling the H-bomb with the development stage that television had reached in 1920." In popular science reports the city of the future is already described as a metropolis with a hydrogen power station located in the middle of a lake of sea water to provide enough current for about ten million inhabitants. It will heat and give light to the whole city, and supply the power for electrically run trains and cars. In fact, a single cubic mile of sea water contains enough deuterium to cover the power needs of the entire globe. However, lake-based power stations for the large cities of the world may be a long way off.

Fortunately, the ocean offers another possibility of obtaining energy which is already being put to use. This possibility is the "pulse beat" of the seas, their tidal motion which has been going on for millions of years. The tides, it has been found, roll 100 billion tons of water into an average bay and draw it out again twice every day. This quantity is seventy times more than the mass that America's mighty Mississippi pours into the Gulf of Mexico. If turbogenerators were built into the entrance of a bay, so that the water would pour through

them with each incoming and outgoing tide, electricity could
be generated very cheaply. French engineers have done precisely this in a Breton bay, not far from Saint-Malo, thus establishing the world's first tidal power station. A dam 760
yards long by 51 yards wide barricades the opening to the
bay. By 1963 the dam should be completed, and yielding annually as much energy as can now be derived from 500,000
tons of coal.

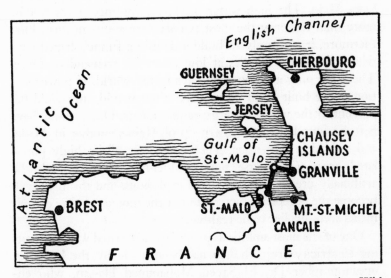

The map shows where the French are completing a tidal power station. With
the help of dams and turbines, the tidal movements of ocean water in the
Bay of Mt.-St.-Michel will be used to produce electricity.

Should this tidal power station prove successful, the
French will build a second one enclosing the whole of the
Bay of Mont-Saint-Michel, an area of 250 square miles, with
a dam 20 miles long. At high tide the waves, measuring some
35 feet, would rush in through sluices and ebb again via the

turbogenerators, producing in one year 50 percent of the electricity France consumed in 1960. Another tidal power station is presently being built on the British island of Saint Mauritius.

Why not utilize the tides throughout the world in a similar manner? After all, two billion horsepower could be generated in this way, an amount equal to one-half of the world's present annual power requirements. Unfortunately, conditions for a tidal power station are not always as favorable as they are at Saint-Malo. The high-water mark, for instance, must not be more than ten or at the most twenty feet above normal. Furthermore, it pays only to build a dam in a funnel-shaped bay, where the water recedes at low tide with tremendous force. There are only a dozen such bays in the world. If power stations were built in all these places they would only yield 0.2 percent of the world's energy requirements. One of these bays is to be found at the northern tip of Maine, another in Alaska and a third in Argentina. They are nearly all in thinly populated areas. Of course more funnel-shaped bays could be artificially created by controlled explosions, and this may well become the accepted practice. But at the moment, other experiments seem likelier to be realized.

One of the most ambitious proposals concerned with generating electricity from the sea has been made by the Egyptian oceanographer Dr. El Sayed Mohammed Hassan, who envisages a dam at a suitable point in the Red Sea. It would be the largest edifice in the world, and would take approximately five years to build. Its purpose would be to prevent any further interchange of water between the Red Sea and the Indian Ocean. A further small barrier with sluices would have to be erected at the end of the Suez Canal to stop any water flowing in from the Mediterranean Sea.

At present about 120,000 cubic feet of water evaporate every second in the Red Sea, but downpours and water flowing in from the Mediterranean Sea and the Indian Ocean continually offset this loss from evaporation. The dam would lower the water level of the Red Sea to the point where water rushing into it from the Indian Ocean through turbines built into the dam would generate ernormous electrical power. If as much water flowed into the sea as evaporated daily, power equal to one-fifth of world production in 1960 could be generated every year.

The Red Sea Dam would bring about an enormous economic improvement for Afro-Asian countries. Hassan estimates that roughly one billion new jobs could be created by providing Saudi Arabia, Israel, Yemen, Jordan, Ethiopia, Somaliland, Sudan, Egypt and even parts of British East Africa and Libya with cheap electricity. It would permit irrigation of the deserts, which in itself would raise the standards of most of these countries.

While man seeks to control the oceans and reaches for "artificial suns" it seems difficult to conceive that he must at the same time turn his attention to a problem of far more immediate importance; namely, the provision of ordinary drinking water. The whole of the human race is threatened by a peril that in previous centuries confronted only Bedouins or people living on the borders of vast deserts: thirst.

The increasing demand for water is beginning to take on serious dimensions. The consequences have already become evident in many industrialized nations, and it will not be long before they will be felt everywhere. Early in 1960 the German Federal Minister of Atomic Energy and Water Supplies, Herr Siegfried Balke, warned that drought would soon sweep across the Federal Republic of Germany. In Israel experts have expressed the opinion that their water deficiency will be dangerous by 1970, when all their natural supplies will either have been tapped or exhausted. The continual disputes between Israel, Jordan and Syria are to a major extent concerned with the fresh water of the Jordan. In Hong Kong the water situation is so serious that its residents, like the inhabitants of the Portuguese province of Macao, had to ask Red China to come to their aid. Irrigation officials in California believe that it is absolutely vital that some plans be made within the next six to eight years to provide enough water to prevent a catastrophe in their area.

A nation's welfare depends on whether it has a lot of water at its disposal or only a little. If it has plenty it will thrive and flourish; too little may mean its downfall. Whoever runs a bath, takes a shower or even cleans his car nowadays uses up hundreds of pints of a liquid which is getting scarcer throughout the world.

The world's seas contain 97.39 percent of all the water on our planet, but unfortunately until very recently it was not possible to make a single cubic foot of the total of 335 million cubic miles drinkable without resorting to a very expensive process of distillation. People had to depend on the fresh water of lakes, rivers and streams, as well as ground water. Although cheap, this water exists only in small quantities as compared to the amount that could be obtained from the sea. Considerable quantities of fresh water exist only in polar regions. Some American geologists have wondered whether it would be possible to use this water for the benefit of mankind, suggesting that icebergs be towed from the Antarctic to the coastlines off the great continents as far north as the Equator. There, pumps could conduct the melting water to the arid regions of California or West Africa.

As an American journalist has said, "It is not difficult to describe a glass of water. But it is impossible to do without it." Very few people have any idea how much precious water is used in every aspect of our daily lives. In America alone the consumption of fresh water amounts to 262 billion gallons per day! About half this amount is used for industrial purposes or hydroelectric power. Modern industry uses fifty times as much water as the total weight of all its raw materials put together. For example, 210,000 gallons of water are needed to produce a single ton of asbestos, 558,000 gallons for a ton of synthetic rubber, 40,000 gallons for a ton of steel or a ton of newsprint. To bring forth a harvest of corn, 562,500 gallons of water per acre are needed. Even alfalfa needs nearly one million gallons per acre, and every pound of beef served at lunch "grew up" on 3,250 gallons of water. Though all this water is put to a useful purpose, there are many instances where water is shamefully wasted. Oklahoma has for years been suffering from a lack of rain. In the summer of 1959 some botanists calculated that the majority of willows in that state consume more ground water daily (over thirty million gallons) than Oklahoma City, with its 244,000 inhabitants, required during the whole of 1958.

Water consumption in America today is seven times higher than at the turn of the century. By 1980, experts have calculated that America will need almost 70 percent more water than she used in 1958, or 432 billion gallons, nineteen times as much as the Colorado River pours into the Gulf of California. Yet by the year 2000, America's 259 million people will have to depend on the same surface water supplies that now serve only 180 million Americans.

Where we should carefully use and preserve our drinking water supplies, we are polluting as well as wasting them. Modern detergents and cleansers, for instance, as used in household and industry, do not disintegrate once they return into the ground through drains and sewers. Instead, they turn up again in ground water in extremely fine dilution, and re-enter the water cycle that flows out of household taps. If sufficiently concentrated, this ground water could be dangerous to health. Many rivers are so polluted by drainage that their water can hardly be called drinkable even after thorough filtering. The lower Rhine is presently so contaminated and salted by industrial waste that it is impossible to tell whether its source was a pure Alpine spring or a metropolitan sewer.

All this points to the dismal conclusion that we are taking water too much for granted, and are using too much of the existing fresh water too unwisely. Efforts to open up new sources of water by means of dams, aqueducts, deep wells and the reuse of water through special filtering processes may remedy the situation for a short time, but they are not the final solution. The fresh water available on the mainland simply will not suffice in the long run to supply man's needs. The rainfall over all the continents is not nearly sufficient to satisfy the fresh water requirements of the inhabitants and in addition refill the subterranean basins. In 1957, an exceptionally dry year, the amount of water used by American industry exceeded the year's rainfall by 10 percent. It was therefore necessary to draw upon subterranean and surface reservoirs.

It is not even possible to use the total rainfall of any single country. Of the 3,762 billion gallons of rain water falling over America every day more than 70 percent evaporates. Of the remaining 30 percent only 525 billion gallons can be turned to industrial or domestic purposes, a quantity which will barely be adequate in 1980. Unless the sea is opened up as a source of fresh water, one dry summer would be enough to bring about a catastrophe such as happened in Western Germany in 1959, when the level of ground water sank so low that nearly 100,000 domestic wells dried up. The cost of water rocketed and fire engines drove around the villages selling water for three to six dollars per two hundred gallons. In some districts, such as Siegen, ration cards had to be distributed entitling every family to one bucket of drinking water per day. On the rivers shipping came to a standstill. The effects of the drought, which caused fruit to wither on the trees, could be felt throughout Europe, right into the summer of 1960.

We cannot be far from the day when fresh water will be drawn from the sea in large quantities. In certain countries where there is a lack of water, agencies and official bodies have been set up to deal with the question of conserving the water supplies and, if possible, raising them, and in 1959 the UN World Health Organization decided to devote most of its efforts to a single program: the provision of a safe water supply for all people.

In the U.S. the agency primarily concerned with salt water conversion is the Office of Saline Water. Since its establishment in 1953 this office has successfully stimulated the development of low-cost saline water conversion processes as well as the construction of the first pilot plants that are already drawing millions of gallons of fresh water from the Pacific and the Atlantic. Major plants are operating or are under construction in Florida, California, North Carolina and Texas.

Distilling sea water to make it drinkable is an old trick. Every sailor knows how to do it and anyone who has suffered shipwreck has attempted it. The principle is easy enough: you evaporate water in the sun, catch the moisture as it rises and let it condense. The result is drinking water free of salt. But while this process can be achieved with relative ease by individuals, it becomes much more difficult when it has to be done for millions of people at the lowest possible cost.

Each of the pilot plants now in operation uses a different principle to convert salt water into fresh water, so that scientists can find out which is the most efficient and economical method. The different processes include solar-heat distillation, distillation with the use of fuels, the membrane process, separation by freezing and other chemical, electrical or physical conversion methods. There are a number of different processes in each of these major groups. Some of them operate on the principle of taking the fresh water out of the salt. Others create drinkable water by taking the salt out of the water.

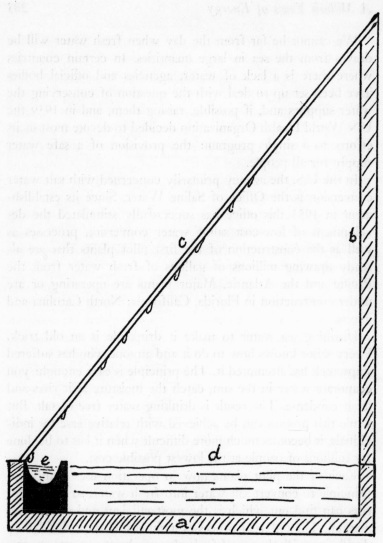

This drawing shows one of the simplest and cheapest methods of obtaining fresh water from the sea. The container (a) is filled with sea water. Sunlight, falling through the slanting pane of glass (c) on to the enclosed box, heats the sea water (d) with the assistance of the reflecting white background (b). The salt water evaporates, leaving the salt residue at the bottom of the vessel. It condenses as fresh water on the glass pane and from there runs down to be caught in the gully (e) from which it can be drawn.

The distillation processes are the most advanced methods in use today besides being the oldest, though several solar distillation pilot units are being operated at comparatively low cost. The sun provides the necessary energy free of charge. The sea water is collected in the basins of troughs covered with glass domes. As soon as the sun strikes them, the atmosphere inside turns to that of a hothouse and the water begins to vaporize; it condenses on the inside of the glass dome and pours down the sides, to be caught as fresh water in a gully just above the floor. Every square yard of the trough yields just one gallon of fresh water daily. This process is especially suitable for tropical countries which have plenty of sunshine and is being given a trial in Australia, Israel and the southern states of America.

Unfortunately, this cheap method of distilling sea water by natural evaporation is the least productive of all. In place of the sun's energy, coal, crude oil or nuclear energy could be used and, of course, H-reactors may one day do the job. The water would be boiled artificially, the steam drawn off and then condensed to fresh water. But heating the water with fuel is not economical, as the amount of energy needed is so great that the cost of a distillation plant would be prohibitive. Approximately 2¼ pounds of oil would be consumed in producing a mere three gallons of fresh water. Research has therefore been directed to making numerous improvements in the distillation of sea water with fuels. Today, with refined equipment, we have reached a stage where something over forty-four gallons of fresh water can be obtained with 2½ pounds of oil.

The so-called membrane process, which uses the method of electrodialisis, will be valuable mainly in the purification of brackish water. It is the property of certain plastic membranes to pass only electrically positive particles (cations), and of other membranes to pass only electrically negative particles (anions). When salts are dissolved in water they break up into equal quantities of cations and anions which move in opposite directions in an electrical field. Thus, the water passing between alternate membrane pairs can be depleted of salt, while that passing through the intervening pairs is enriched. If the process is repeated often enough, salt-free drinking water can be obtained.

Attempts are also being made to freeze salt water and then separate the salt-free ice crystals from the brine. Although this process has not yet been scaled up to production-size operations in the United States, its economic potential makes it very attractive, and every effort is being made to improve the technology of the process. Whereas in 1939 it used to cost about five dollars to convert a thousand gallons of sea water into fresh water, it now costs anywhere between thirty-eight cents and a dollar per thousand gallons. Even this appears expensive when one considers that the same amount of water from conventional sources costs only ten or twenty cents in many parts of the United States. The comparison, however, is deceptive, since the latter price is paid for fresh water still easily obtained. Once water from conventional sources becomes scarce, its price will rise considerably, while the cost of converting sea water will continue to drop thanks to new and improved processes.

Ideally, the power needed to convert a thousand gallons of brine into fresh water would be 2.8 kilowatt hours, but for several technical reasons such conditions can never be realized. (In practice it generally takes about 12 kilowatt hours to yield one thousand gallons of fresh water.) Early in 1960, the Russian engineer, Alexander Zarchin, who started experimenting with the freezing process as a refugee in Israel, maintained that he had discovered the cheapest way of obtaining fresh water using only 3.5 kilowatt hours per thousand gallons. At his secret demonstration plant near Tel Aviv salt water is drawn from the sea at one end while at the other fresh water flows out into the desert. The Israeli government was so enthusiastic about the new process that after a demonstration plans were published in 1960 for the construction of two big conversion plants. The Israelis even considered selling a patent license to Egypt! The two new plants are to be built near the port of Elath on the Gulf of Aqaba, where each will daily produce 500,000 gallons of fresh water. The cost, according to the American industrialist, David Karr, will be a mere twenty cents per thousand gallons.

American scientists have recently turned their attention to the way nature herself converts salt water. Since the end of 1959, they have been hoping to solve the problem in the least expensive way by using algae instead of costly modern machinery to turn sea water into drinking water. Algae, it has been found, store up salt during the daytime, and release it to the surrounding water at night. "If we transplant seaweed into a sea-water basin," said the American biologist, Gilbert V. Levin, "it would extract some of the salt during the day. We could then remove it from the basin with grapples or grating and transfer it to a second basin filled with brackish water, where it is dark. The seaweed would start disposing of its salt. After a while we would bring it back to the first lake where it would extract another pinch of salt. Again it would be brought to the 'night basin,' which by then will have been replenished with brackish water. This process can be repeated until the original sea water in the first lake is desalted. A fully automatic seaweed plant would presumably run at a cheaper rate than all the other monster plants. Repairs would be quite unnecessary, for the 'machines' would continually renovate themselves and reproduce."

Many American communities hope to build their own conversion plants in the course of the next twenty years. "Fresh water from the sea is already more of a reality today than many

people think," explained W. Sherman Gilliam, of the Office
of Saline Water early in 1960.

Several communities throughout the world find that it is
already more economical to get their fresh water from the sea
than to draw upon natural mainland reservoirs. When American
engineers in Kuwait, the rich oil state on the Persian Gulf,
erected a plant several years ago to produce fresh water for
cleaning their wells, the sheik of Kuwait was so impressed
by the "water machine" that he had one built for his subjects
at his own expense. It produces 2.5 million gallons of fresh
water from the Persian Gulf every day. A second plant will
be completed shortly.

The inhabitants of Aruba, an island in the Caribbean, also
get their fresh water from the sea. The plant's daily output
of 3.5 million gallons is more than enough to quench their
thirst.

Coalinga in California also has built its own salt-water conversion plant with a daily output of 26,000 gallons of fresh
water. The cost per thousand gallons comes to not more than
fifty cents. This is cheap, considering that the people of Coalinga previously had to pay up to seven dollars for the same
amount.

"By 1980 hundreds of towns and communities in many parts
of America will probably be drawing all their fresh water
from the sea," predicted Fred G. Aandahl of the U.S. Department of the Interior.

16   Will Man Poison the Sea?

Man has hardly begun to put the sea to useful purposes, but he has already started to rob himself of the last and greatest source of raw materials by poisoning it!

One afternoon in July of 1959 a few beachcombers walking along the Pacific Coast near Port Orford, Oregon, came across a peculiar-looking steel drum. Written on it were the letters A.E.C. and the warning: "Danger—radioactive material." The barrel, washed ashore by the tide, contained radioactive "garbage," the safe disposal of which has become one of the greatest problems of a growing atomic industry.

Mildly criticizing the situation, a popular American news magazine stated that "in the U.S. any delicate objects that the Government has wanted to do away with have for years been packed in boxes, tied up, and sunk in the deep blue sea." As long as obsolete armaments of the Second World War were involved, this unusual disposal practice seemed reasonable and quite in place. Since 1946, however, the Atomic Energy Commission has also been dumping approximately 45,000 old oil drums, filled with radioactive waste, into the sea at various points along the U.S. coast. Many of America's big rivers also serve as drains for this atomic garbage.

The English Atomic Energy Authority has found a similar solution for its nuclear power station at Windscale. For years, the station's radioactive wastes have been pumped into the Irish Sea through a three-mile pipe line. More recently, the French Government also announced plans to dump "hot" (radioactive) waste into the Mediterranean between Antibes and Calvi on the island of Corsica. The residents of the Riviera quite understandably shudder at the thought of what this would do to the tourist trade.

The other Western nations with nuclear industries are all considering the use of the sea along their coasts as dumping grounds for the unpleasant by-products of the atomic age. By so doing, man may destroy his ultimate source of raw materials even before he has begun to benefit from it. He may be poisoning the spawning grounds of large shoals of fish, thereby unintentionally destroying one of the resources on which he will eventually depend most heavily. He may be fouling his own nest, as he has with industrial sewers, air pollution and fallout from nuclear tests which shower radioactive particles over the earth for months thereafter.

The problem with radioactive waste is that it is not rubbish in the usual sense. It cannot simply be thrown away, burnt or buried. The threat of radiation persists. Even as it dries up or decays into dust, it continues to emit dangerous radioactive particles for a certain length of time, ranging anywhere from a few hours to several thousand years. "Atomic garbage" dropped into the sea is the sort of radioactive fallout which has not been as much in the headlines as that from atmospheric explosions, especially the recent series of Soviet nuclear tests. The only real difference between the two is that fallout, blown high into the stratosphere and then dispersed by the winds over great areas of the world, is the result of *uncontrolled* nuclear reactions, whereas radioactive waste is a by-product of *controlled* nuclear reactions. This waste is not dispersed over a wide area, but is—for a while at least—safely contained in the laboratory. Made up of broken test equipment, contaminated lab coats, carcasses of "guinea pigs" and, above all, still active material for which there is no further use, it can be solid, liquid or gaseous. These forms of waste may be slightly radioactive or highly radioactive, but in whatever form, they all have one thing in common: unlike the radioactive particles of aerial fallout, they can be regulated and kept in check by the man who decides what to do with them.

There are two broad methods of dealing with radioactive waste. One is to concentrate and store it, the other to dilute and disperse it. The first method is used primarily for high-level waste, which may remain active for hundreds, even thousands, of years. This waste, in liquid form, is generally stored in stainless steel tanks and kept under strict guard. Giant containers, some of which hold nearly one million gallons of the dangerous brew, today stand in mountain dungeons by the Savannah River in South Carolina, in Idaho and in Washington. Each of these tanks, which require special refrigeration plants to carry away the heat that always accompanies the decay of radioactive material, is erected at very high cost. Construction and maintenance of the tanks alone ran to $110 million, while the storage of every gallon of the boiling waste costs the U.S. taxpayer another $1.50 per year. From 1945 to 1960, more than 65 million gallons of high-level liquid waste were accumulated, and the gigantic quantities of this expensive but useless substance grow from day to day as the arms race continues with increasing momentum. By the end of 1961 the total amount of land-buried waste had risen from 316,000 cubic feet in 1955 to 1,125,000 cubic feet.

This accumulation of high-level radioactive waste is exceeded, though, by the low-level wastes produced each year. Dr. E. G. Struxness, a nuclear scientist, described this very bluntly: "In a few years' time there will be so many proc-

essing factories and nuclear reactors that we shall be up to our
necks in radioactive waste if we don't find suitable places or
cheap methods of getting rid of it." As a consequence, many
nuclear scientists were, and still are, in favor of releasing
low-level radioactive waste into the environment, as the concentration and containing of this enormous quantity of dangerous material would be extremely costly. Gaseous wastes, for
instance, have for years been carefully filtered before being
ejected into the atmosphere where the winds disperse them.
More expensive as a method than the disposal of low-level
liquid wastes, which are simply released into rivers (such as
the Columbia and the Mohawk) or poured directly into the
ground, it is also probably more efficient than the practice of
mixing liquid wastes with concrete and solid wastes, then
packing them into fifty-five-gallon steel drums to be dumped
into the sea.

Public attention was focused on this practice in 1959 when
the National Academy of Sciences prepared a report on
*Radioactive Waste Disposal into Atlantic and Gulf Coastal
Waters* at the request of the AEC. In this report twenty-eight
tentative sites for offshore dumping of low-level radioactive
wastes were suggested.

The oceanographers who prepared the report took a very
cautious line in their recommendations. Though they assumed
that the population of the neighboring coastal regions would
live exclusively on fish in the course of the next five hundred
years and that every drum of waste would eventually break
open on the sea floor, they estimated that quantities of radioactive wastes could be safely disposed in certain dumping
grounds seventy-five miles apart from one another.

However, the public was aroused. It was outraged to learn
that thousands upon thousands of steel drums with "atomic
garbage" had for years been dumped off the Massachusetts,
New Jersey, Texas and California coasts, sometimes in less

than fifty fathoms of water. The AEC hurried to explain that this disposal method was completely safe (though the drum washed ashore in Oregon seems to contradict this assertion). The AEC further maintained that the drums had a life expectancy of ten years, by which time the radioactive contents would have completely decayed into harmlessness, and that the containers were strong enough to withstand the impact when they hit the bottom.

Tests with simulated radioactive waste were conducted, which seemed to confirm these statements. In April, 1959, the AEC sent a few frogmen to the sea floor off Massachusetts, with color-movie cameras, to observe fourteen drums filled with "waste" (actually yellow dye). The drums were filmed by divers as they were dumped into the sea and fell to the bottom at a speed of 20 mph. Not one of them burst, nor did one drop of "radioactive" dye seep out.

Impressive as this test may appear, it does not provide final proof. Fourteen undamaged drums out of tens of thousands that have been dumped may be no more than a mere coincidence. Contrary to dye, radioactivity can, of course, penetrate through the walls of even an undamaged drum. But, Dr. Irvin E. Wallen of the AEC maintains, the amount would be so slight that a fish would have to remain close to it for a considerable length of time before any genetic damage was caused. "It is even more improbable that the very fish affected by the radiation should be caught by fishermen," says Wallen.

Again, to verify these and other assumptions, the AEC conducted careful examinations of the immediate neighborhoods of former dumping grounds. Divers obtained and tested water samples and half-inch layers of sea deposits from the ocean floor, along with seaweed, crabs and molluscs, which concentrate a variety of minerals, including radioactive substances, in their bodies. They found no signs of any increase over the normal amount of radioactivity. "The hottest thing on board our research ship was the dial of my watch," said one of the scientists taking part in the project.

After all this research, many nuclear scientists argue with conviction that the disposal of radioactive wastes in the sea is "absolutely safe." They claim that as the disposal is carefully guided by rules of maximum permissible levels for human exposure, the wastes introduced into the oceans cannot substantially alter the natural radioactivity of the sea. Unfortunately, the "maximum permissible levels" set up by various national and international bodies are not unanimously recognized as safe levels. Just as in the question of fallout, scientists still disagree where the danger begins. Some geneticists believe that even a few curies can present a threat. On the other hand, the British Atomic Authority thinks it still safe to drain waste products of the order of ten thousand curies per month into the Irish Sea. Even this amount seems small when compared to the one million curies that nuclear ships are likely to discharge into the ocean each year after 1975, unless proper controls or regulations are agreed to on an international basis before that time.

Though most of these materials, like the wastes of the Windscale plant, will be short-lived (i.e., will decay in a relatively brief period), the long-range effects of their induction into the sea are far from clear. Will the currents really dilute them as quickly and thoroughly as it is hoped? Will they really be harmless to plant and animal life? At present, no one can tell with certainty whether the liquid wastes sent to the ocean bottom in steel drums will not be harmful in the long run.

The AEC maintains that these wastes will remain isolated from the upper regions of the water for at least several decades, and possibly even for several centuries. The opinion is based on the long-held views of many Western oceanographers that it takes 600, in some regions of the sea even 2,300, years before the water at the greatest depths reaches the surface, where life abounds in profusion. On this precise point, Eastern and Western opinions diverge. What the Western scientists have long regarded as a safety factor, namely the movements of deep-sea water, the Russians regard as dangerous.

Deep-sea water is neither still nor sluggish, but rather in a state of unceasing movement and intermingling, Russian oceanographers explain. Currents and the circulation of deep layers of water is one thing that the Soviets have tried to explore more thoroughly than any other nation between 1954 and 1959. During the International Geophysical Year, it was they who discovered submarine currents, at depths of up to 6½ miles, mightier than the Amazon. In many places on the deep-sea floor they have photographed ripples such as are to be seen at low tide in shallow waters, a sign that the water is in continuous motion there. From these and countless other observations they reached the conclusion that the oceans are composed of graduated layers and that there is a fairly active vertical motion going on up to a depth of more than 35,000 feet.

Professor R. A. Moisseyev of the Russian Academy of Science adds that "radioactive waste matter escaping from a container at a great depth would therefore not stay put or only rise slowly but would mix with other water and quickly get into the zones flooded with light and abundant with life near the surface. This process takes only forty to sixty years, too short a period to render the radioactive particles in the water free from danger." Like most of his Soviet colleagues Moisseyev is against the dumping of even the weakest radioactive waste into the sea. In the West, recently, Professor Auguste Piccard also expressed fear that radioactive waste buried in the deep sea could contaminate the entire body of the water around the globe. "Nobody seems to know whether the containers with the atomic waste can really withstand the enormous pressure to which they are exposed on the ocean floor.

Currents could raise the radioactive material from even the deepest zones of the sea to the surface, if it were to escape from one of the containers."

The divergence of opinions on the safety of disposal of radioactive wastes in the sea received its clearest formulation in November of 1959 during the international congress of nuclear scientists in Monaco, in which oceanographers also took part. The congress failed to set up an International Control Authority to deal with the question of radioactive waste disposal, as the three hundred scientists from thirty-three countries failed to agree on whether it was more dangerous to bury radioactive waste in the ground or sink it in the sea. The atomic energy commissions of both England and the United States are thus allowed to continue to use the Atlantic and Pacific as dumping grounds for their radioactive waste. There was unanimity on only one point, and that was that the whole complex question needed continued investigation in the most thorough manner, and that such investigation should be carried out with no delay, a view often strongly expressed in the research programs of American oceanographers.

The main area of exploration remains the study of the genetic effect of radioactive radiation on marine organisms. We know that the more complicated the organism, the more sensitive it will be to radiation. From experiments we also know that zooplankton and phytoplankton are the first to absorb most radioactive particles that get into the water and will thus become a kind of radiation source in themselves. As they are important links in the marine food chain, they can gradually influence all the higher forms of life in the sea which feed on them and on one another. Results obtained so far have been based mainly on experiments conducted in lakes, and on observations carried out in the ocean after nuclear tests. (In the latter case, contamination was a result of fallout—not waste disposal.) Still, it is interesting to learn a few details about these observations since they well illustrate the possible dangers of large-scale radioactive waste disposal in the sea.

For several years the AEC, for instance, had discharged large amounts of partially purified liquid waste into a fresh-water lake near Oak Ridge. It was later found that the fish in the lake grew more slowly and died younger than was normal for the species. One species died out altogether, another was on the verge of extinction. The concentration of Strontium 90 (a radioactive isotope) in the bone structure of the surviving fish was twenty to thirty thousand times higher than that found in the lake itself.

Other observations were made in the Pacific several years after the U.S. H-bomb tests of 1954. It was found that certain predatory fish showed a higher degree of concentration of radioactive substances in their organisms than marine creatures of lower species. In their bones and skin the concentration was twice as high as in their flesh. It was eighteen times as high in their livers, while it was as much as thirty-six to seventy-two times as high in their alimentary tracts. This clearly indicates that radioactivity, absorbed by the plankton immediately after the H-bomb explosion, had gotten into the food chain and finally found its way to one of the highest types of animals of that area. The fish had become dangerous for human consumption. Similarly, the inhabitants of the Pacific island of Rongelap had to be persauded, in 1959, not to catch any more coconut crabs, for investigation had shown that these important protein suppliers for the islanders had stored up so much radioactivity in their cells that five years after the H-bomb tests they were dangerous to eat.

Obviously a tremendous amount of research is still needed before radioactive waste disposal into the sea appears justified. Several programs in this direction have been planned or are under way. To discover, for instance, how marine life would react to radioactive waste over a period of many years, scientists have suggested injecting small quantities of "atomic garbage" into a Pacific lagoon. In this way conditions that would exist in the seas of the world after several decades of waste dumping could be reproduced on a smaller scale. The condition of the water in and around the lagoon could be examined, and in the course of only several years these studies would show how radioactivity of low-level waste affects marine life and whether it causes any detrimental changes over several generations.

To determine in greater detail if and how radioactive particles are moved by ocean currents, the AEC plans to dye parts of the North Atlantic pink. In the summer of 1962, its scientists intend to dump a certain amount of "Rhodamine B," a commercial dye, into the waters off Bermuda. With special instruments, so sensitive that they can detect one part of dye to fifty billion parts of water, the course that the "Rhodamine B" travels can be charted. The experiment may provide oceanographers with a new tool to trace the course that any radioactive waste dumped into a particular part of the sea may take, and thus help to fashion a new policy for its disposal at sea. It will also help oceanographers understand a bit better the complicated flow of ocean currents. All this brings one step nearer the day when man will be using these very same currents to change the climate, not only of individual countries but, possibly, of entire continents.

17 Damming the Sea

Leading oceanographers are convinced that before long it will be possible to divert the course of mighty ocean currents by means of large dams or pumping plants. In the words of an enthusiastic Russian civil engineer, Nicolai Romanov, "We will change the surface of our planet. We will tame the oceans and force the great currents into other tracks. We shall even create artificial seas." In 1959, some Soviet oceanographers and meteorologists declared more soberly that "We are not satisfied with the present course of many currents," and then went so far as to talk about "serious faults" in the construction of the planet.

Wherever ocean currents lie within their territorial waters, the Russians intend quite seriously to make extensive alterations in their course. They are already at the stage where numerous projects have been drawn up. By the year 2000, for example, they intend to join the island of Sakhalin to the mainland of Russia by means of a dam. Western engineers are not very far behind in suggesting similar projects. Years ago, proposals were made to build a dam across the shallow waters of Newfoundland, and to close the Strait of Gibraltar with a concrete "plug." Plans for an enormous dam across the North Atlantic between Norway and Greenland no longer shock an audience familiar with such grandiose proposals.

These structures would represent a relatively cheap way of

obtaining climatic changes, not only for the countries bordering on the seas but presumably over entire continents. It is estimated that to produce the power of an average hurricane one million times as much electric current as is currently used in the United States per year would be needed. Similarly, it would take the energy of twelve power stations, each with the capacity of the massive Hoover Dam, to move the air over Los Angeles at a speed of only 10 mph. Yet a single dam erected at a strategic spot in the ocean would be enough to divert the course of a warm or cold ocean current, and thereby influence the weather at the interior of bordering countries, prevent the formation or change the direction of hurricanes or send rain clouds over arid deserts.

This means that with comparatively little technical effort the circulation of currents in all the oceans—and with it the climate as well—could possibly be made subject to man's will. We can also assume that this capacity would prove the deadliest of all weapons, for whoever could influence the weather, whoever could keep winds and storms in a Pandora's box could blanket an enemy continent with such natural catastrophes as to make counterattack impossible.

Before seriously considering the practical realization of such plans, we must look at something far more important than the technical problems involved in the building of dams of this kind. We must first of all know the effects of these kinds of climatic changes. What will happen to an ocean current when it is diverted by a dam? Will it warm one coastline and cover another region with a thick crust of ice?

Our knowledge of the climatic influences of ocean currents is still very scanty. In the opinion of certain reputable meteorologists, we have no ability whatsoever to forecast the weather with complete certainty for lengthy periods. No one knows precisely what the weather will be like over a given land or continent in the year 2000, nor even in 1980 or 1990, and construction of a dam in the sea cannot be attempted until we possess fuller knowledge of the sea and its movements. American oceanographers believe that, in theory, we could be this far advanced by 1970. By then, they hope to have settled at least one of their present basic problems: how and why do the ocean waters move?

In 1962 we know only in the most general way that the sea acts like a thermostat. It absorbs about one-third of the energy reaching our planet through the sun's rays, and distributes it throughout the globe by various processes: by evaporation as the liquid water changes to vapor, by condensation as the vapor drops again as rain. But the major job of energy distribution is performed by vertical and horizontal ocean currents. Like arteries in a gigantic organism, they transport masses of cold and warm water as well as air pregnant with humidity to the four corners of the earth. Ocean currents affect the direction of the wind and storms. A great part of the energy needed to drive the wind comes from sea water evaporating in tropical latitudes. How these processes develop individually, how they are connected and influence each other remain unsolved problems.

Shortly before the beginning of the International Geophysical Year, scientists recognized that they knew so little about the circulation of water in the ocean that no one could say whether it takes one hundred or ten thousand years for the deep-sea water of the Antarctic icecap to reach the Equator and return. For a long time, almost nothing was known about the currents that move deep below the surface of the sea. Yet this knowledge is essential for long-range weather forecasts, and indispensable for the building of the giant dams of the future.

It was not until after the last war that oceanographers made their greatest discovery about the movement of sea water. They found that powerful currents flow at certain depths below the surface, moving at different speeds than their counterparts on the surface immediately above them, which often flow in the opposite direction. The study of this vast and complex process is only just beginning. Nevertheless, by early 1960, four submarine currents had already been discovered, each a thousand times more powerful than the Rhine, the Nile or the Mississippi. Although we are still ignorant of their origins and of the full extent of their courses, the discovery of these currents is impressive enough to suggest the nature of future investigations.

The Cromwell Stream, discovered south of Hawaii in 1951, has properties which can only be described as gigantic. It is believed to originate somewhere near the Gilbert Islands, and to end more than eight thousand miles away, not far from the Galápagos Islands. Nearly a hundred miles wide, it carries three times as much water as the Gulf Stream, flowing at a depth of five hundred feet along the Equator, where it sometimes reaches a speed of three knots. The Russians are especially interested in this current, as it means that any of their submarines using the stream would very quickly get within striking distance of the American continent. For a submarine that runs at ten knots, this current means as much as a 110 mph tail wind does for a modern jet airliner. It can bring it quicker to its destination.

Apparently an equally important but much weaker deep-sea current flows through the Atlantic under the Gulf Stream. It was first noticed in 1957, when American oceanographers lowered moving radio buoys into depths varying between 4,400 feet and 9,000 feet. The buoys moved into a southerly direction, i.e., opposite to the direction of the Gulf Stream itself. In this way a tremendous amount of water is exchanged daily between the North and the South Atlantic.

These discoveries, together with the Russian disclosure that there is a relatively strong movement in water even at the greatest depths, shed a completely new light on former theories about the movement of ocean currents. It became obvious that winds alone could not be responsible for the great currents, as winds affect only the surface layer to a depth of some three hundred feet. Deep-sea currents, it is now theorized, are the result of very slight variations in the density of the sea water at different depths. Therefore thousands upon thousands of readings of the temperature and salinity of different regions of the sea are needed before we can expect to understand the system of ocean currents and their influence on the climate.

This presents great problems in obtaining and coordinating the relevant information. In the course of their work, oceanographers occasionally learn something from unexpected sources. For instance, when in July, 1959, an American cosmetics firm poured $30,000 worth of perfume into the Gulf Stream off Miami for advertising purposes, the oceanographic faculty of the local university was immediately on the scene. The perfume was an excellent medium for learning more about the course, speed and extent of the warm Gulf Stream water. By Christmas of that year the scent had reached the British Isles.

Officials of the U.S. Coast and Geodetic Survey make use of a far older and more usual practice. Each year they throw hundreds of corked bottles into the sea, and from the wanderings of these bottles obtain information about currents near the mainland. Some of these bottles are meant to sink to the bottom straightaway. If they are found at places some distance away, they indicate some new strong water movement on the sea floor. Occasionally they are borne halfway round the world. During World War I an American soldier threw a bottle containing a letter into the Atlantic on his way to France. Almost forty-two years later, in 1959, it was washed up on the beach of Tasmania.

Despite or because of its quaintness, the empty-bottle

method is being left behind by more effective and modern techniques. Mobile radio buoys, for example, let down to various depths, will emit constant acoustic signals, which can be followed by surface ships charting their course with the aid of hydrophones, in the same way as a destroyer pursues submarines. In the spring of 1960, the American submarine *Archerfish* set out on a world-wide voyage with oceanographers on board to test this method and "shadow" various submarine currents. Within the next decade, all these methods are expected to contribute to a clearer and fuller picture of the movement of ocean currents.

Another phenomenon presently under intensive investigation, which seems to be caused by the mysterious motion of the ocean's water, is the rising and falling of the sea level. This apparently has to do, not with the tides, as was previously supposed, but rather with the season of the year. It has been observed that in the winter the ocean shrinks a little, expanding again in the summer. In the seas of the Northern Hemisphere the rise along the coast amounts to some eight inches, or to a total of several thousand cubic miles of water between March and September. Where does this water come from? The summer rise in the North can be traced in part to the seasonal warming of the water. When great quantities of sea water are deposited on the mainland in the form of snow every winter, the oceans shrivel up correspondingly. American scientists believe, however, that there are also certain, possibly unknown, currents which transport considerable quantities of water across the Equator each season. This annual shift of weight would be sufficient to cause a calculable swaying effect as the earth revolves, which in its turn could affect the climate.

These phenomena, which we have only recently discovered, indicate how many factors must be studied before steps to control the weather by artificial means can be taken. Americans are presently involved in research to determine whether the many projects on the drawing boards will produce the desired climatic changes. The Russians have far fewer doubts about their own dam-building projects, and are moving ahead at what is perhaps reckless speed. By means of a dam they intend to warm up the island of Sakhalin located between northern Japan and the east coast of Siberia, which has a wealth of crude oil, coal, gold and other valuable mineral deposits, but also an unfavorable climate which makes mining difficult and most of the island uninhabitable. In the north, surrounded by the Sea of Okhotsk, it is cold and foggy, with an unusually high rainfall all year round. The Tatar Straits between the island and the mainland of eastern Siberia are only navigable in the high summer season. In winter they are frozen over by a layer of ice three feet thick. The southern part of the island, however, surrounded by the warmer Sea of Japan, enjoys a comfortable climate.

At every high tide a certain amount of warm water pours through the Tatar Straits, flowing from the warm Sea of Japan into the cold Sea of Okhotsk. However, the effect of this warm water on the north of the island is negligible as it immediately flows back again with the ensuing low tide. Russian engineers intend to build a wide dam across the narrowest part of the Tatar Straits. Six gigantic gates, each 330 feet wide, will be built into the dam in such a way that they only open in the direction of the Sea of Okhotsk at the beginning of every high tide. The warm water, rushing into the northern half of the straits from the Sea of Japan, will force these gates open. As soon as the tide begins to ebb the gates will automatically lock, so that the warm water can no longer flow back. With this process repeated at every high tide, nearly forty thousand cubic feet of warm water (four times the amount the Volga, Don and Dnieper daily pour into the seas) will reach the northern coast of the island and the coast of the mainland of Siberia every twenty-four hours.

The average temperature on the coast of the Sea of Okhotsk may gradually rise by 18° Fahrenheit, and even in winter the ice barrier would probably lie much further north than it does today. Not only Sakhalin but the whole of the east coast of Siberia stands to benefit by such climatic changes. Japan, however, protested as soon as this plan was made known. It claimed that the warm Kuroshio Stream would move further north as a result of the warming of the Sea of Okhotsk, a change that naturally would have detrimental effects on Japan.

An equally ambitious plan for controlling the seas is the West's Atlantropa Project, aimed at lowering the sea level of the Mediterranean. More important, however, than the original objective of the project—winning land back from the sea—is a far-reaching side effect which has been recognized as a result of recent American research, and which has to do with a gradual warming of the whole Northern Hemisphere.

More water evaporates annually from the Mediterranean than the Nile, the Po and other rivers can add to it. The deficit is largely made up by the flow of water from the Atlantic and the Black Sea. As far back as the twenties, Heinrich Soergel, the German civil engineer, suggested blocking the Dardanelles and the Strait of Gibraltar with dams. Because of extensive evaporation, the level of the Mediterranean would then fall by four and a half feet per year. After about 140 years the Mediterranean would be some 660 feet "lower" than it is today, opening another 150 million acres of fertile land around the coasts to cultivation. This would put most of the present water ports out of use, but by that time ships might be replaced by more modern vehicles in any case.

Soergel believed that the great differences between the levels of the Atlantic and the Mediterranean could then be used to generate electric energy. Fifty billion cubic feet of Atlantic water shooting through the turbine shafts of the Gibraltar Dam into the Mediterranean every year would yield some 500 billion kilowatt hours, to provide power for hundreds of new agricultural areas in North Africa.

American studies of the circulation of water in the world's seas carried out in 1959 show that the Gibraltar Dam would have far more extensive effects than Soergel could possibly have imagined, for an extremely salty deep-sea current flows into the Atlantic from the Mediterranean and is responsible for the fact that the Atlantic is one of the saltiest of oceans. Many oceanographers think the Gibraltar Dam would prevent this current from getting into the Atlantic, thus causing its salt content to drop. Thirty years after the dam was built, the Atlantic would probably not be much saltier than the Pacific is at present. The density of the Atlantic water would fall correspondingly. Since this would make it lighter, masses of water near the Arctic would no longer sink from the surface to the sea floor, as happens today. According to the American oceanographer Henry Stommel, only cold Antarctic waters would continue to "feed" the different deep-sea currents. The Gibraltar Dam would thus considerably alter the circulation of the deep sea, not in a short space of time perhaps, but certainly in the course of centuries. What would be the results?

If the Arctic waters no longer sank to the ocean floor the warm water of the Gulf Stream would no longer run to Norway and the Arctic.

At different times, there have been plans for using currents, guided by dams, in other parts of the ocean to influence climate. One project that has been considered is the diversion of the Labrador Stream from its regular course. This cold Canadian current flows southward along the East Coast of the United States, driving the Gulf Stream from the coast into the Atlantic Ocean. If the Labrador Stream could be stopped from flowing south, it has been reasoned, the result would be milder East Coast winters. A demand for the necessary funds to erect such a dam was put before Congress in

Washington as far back as 1912, but the proposed project immediately aroused world-wide protest. Opponents of the plan argued that the only consequence would be foggier rather than warmer New York winters, which would disrupt shipping and commerce.

Recently another controversy arose over the Soviet proposal that a dam be built in the Bering Strait. At the prodding of Alaska's Senator Ernest Gruening, Congress in 1959 gave serious consideration to a proposal by the Russian engineer, Peter Borissov. "The Soviet Union is offering us the possibility not only of melting the ice of the North Pole, but the ice of the cold war as well," said Gruening. "Carrying it out would open up a new continent and be a blessing for all the lands of the Northern Hemisphere."

Vast stretches of northern Siberia, Alaska and Canada are covered with ice and snow for more than half the year. The temperature falls to lower than 48° Fahrenheit. People cannot live in these areas nor is any form of agriculture or fishing possible because of frost. These agriculturally dead zones are amazingly large and comprise about 47 percent of the Soviet Union (almost half of the Red Empire) and as much as 70 percent of Alaska.

"All the same, these very regions could be made into a farmer's paradise," Borissov believes. "All we have to do is to melt the ice of the North Polar Sea. What causes these northern areas to freeze up continually is both the cold Labrador Stream and the East Greenland Stream. They meet the warm Gulf Stream in the Arctic and force it deep down underneath the polar ice, where it is no longer effective enough to melt the ice. The only way of melting the ice is to build a dam through the Bering Strait. We could then pump the cold water out of the Arctic Basin and replace it with warm water from the Pacific."

Borissov's dam would be built at that part of the Bering

Strait where the average depth is not more than 160 feet. From the Siberian Chukchi Peninsula it would stretch forty-six miles across to the Prince of Wales Cape in Alaska. Erection of the dam could begin with the construction of large concrete caissons on both the U.S. and the Soviet sides. These caissons, resembling enormous troughs, would then be towed over the future foundation line of the dam, filled with mud by dredges and sunk to the bottom, where they would be anchored by divers. Several thousands of these caissons would be needed for the foundation of the dam. With this phase of construction completed, the wall itself could be built out of reinforced concrete.

Unlike reservoir walls, the walls of the dam across the Bering Strait would not have to resist any great pressures, and could house within themselves the enormous turbine pumps which would pass the warm surface water of the Pacific through long pipes into the Arctic Ocean, generating enormous heat. At the same time, other pumps would suck in the cold, deeper water of the Arctic Ocean and force it into the depths of the Pacific. The waters of the Gulf Stream, flowing more freely into the Arctic Ocean, would gradually start to break up the ice of these regions.

"The result of this little bit of interference in the oceanographic machinery of our earth I have worked out exactly," Borissov told the Polytechnicum in Moscow in 1958. "The average temperature at the North Pole would rise by about 27° Fahrenheit. This rise of temperature would lengthen the warm season. Important polar regions could be given over to agriculture, and the rivers of Alaska, Siberia and Canada would be navigable the whole year round. New agricultural areas will have been created."

Most engineers agree that the actual building of the dam should present no technical difficulties. If all the northern lands cooperate in the project there should be no financial problems either. "I have estimated the cost at seventy billion rubles [about twenty billion dollars]," says Borissov. "That is just about twice as much as the Soviet Union has spent in past years on making her far eastern provinces fertile. In addition a dam across the Bering Strait really is the cheapest and most profitable way of melting the Arctic ice. All other methods would prove too expensive or would fall through altogether." (American atomic scientists had previously suggested melting the ice at both poles with H-bombs.)

"As soon as the frozen surface has disappeared, it will become immediately warmer in the extreme north," Borissov maintains. "Once it has melted, not so much sunlight can be reflected, and the open Arctic water will then begin absorbing the heat. This additional warmth alone is 150 times more than that generated by all the industrial plants in the world in 1960."

With an Arctic Ocean free from ice, all sorts of advantages would ensue. A new, large, ice-free transport route of five billion square miles would be created. In Borissov's view the banks of fog and the dangerous icebergs would disappear. The most important result, however, would be that vast areas of land would come into productive use for all countries bordering on the icy sea, with the year-round temperature equivalent to the Ukraine in January, making the Arctic a distinctly warm sea region. The climate of countries further south would alter as well, for the earth's "weather kitchen" lies in northern Siberia. It is here that the cold depressions, winds and the storms have their origin. The masses of cold air which hang over the Pole and escape to Europe and North America every winter would no longer arise if the Arctic were heated. The northern American states would have a winter as mild as the Riviera, the central states the kind of temperature that Florida enjoys. All this could result in tremendous agricultural, industrial and population changes and shifts.

"The favorable influence of my dam would be felt throughout the whole world," Borissov believes. But he would not be a genuine scientist if he did not admit the many objections to his gigantic weather plan. Such objections have been raised not only by Western experts but also by some Russian colleagues. For instance, the meteorologist Dimitri Drogaizev says, "If we were to warm the Arctic it could be that the climate would deteriorate in the south instead of improving. The summers would get even drier and the winters colder. True, we would get luscious meadows in the far north, but aridity would presumably also creep further north."

Many Western experts believe that the effects of the dam would be noticeable in the Bering Strait and nowhere else. It would get warmer there when no further exchange of water in the Pacific with the cold Arctic water was possible. And since mainly westerly winds blow across the Bering Strait they would take part of the warmth to southern Alaska.

Gordon Lill, the director of the Geophysical Department of the Naval Research Institute, doubts whether the dam conceived by Borissov could warm the Arctic Ocean at all. "Enormous masses of water would have to be pumped from the Pacific to the ice, and the Gulf Stream has already cooled off so much when it gets to the extreme north that its water is hardly capable of warming the Arctic to any degree."

Borissov's plan can be neither accepted nor condemned until the climatic effects of such a dam are determined by research on an international basis. Before it can be said that a dam through the Bering Straits will be a blessing to mankind, we must carry out a detailed investigation of the effects of such a "blockade." Then we shall see whether several dams are needed in various parts of the ocean to achieve the favorable climatic changes that Borissov hopes to bring about with one dam.

18 A Second Flood— and a Second Ice Age

While Borissov proposes to build a dam to melt the Arctic ice-cap, coming generations may be forced to erect a dam precisely for the opposite purpose: to keep the Arctic Ocean from melting and drowning ports like London, Oslo, Hamburg, and even New York, in the waves of a new flood.

If the theories of the American geophysicist Professor Maurice Ewing of the Lamont Geophysical Laboratory and his colleague Dr. William L. Donn are correct, the great European and American coastal towns will be swallowed by the waters of the Atlantic in about a hundred years. Not long after that the Arctic glaciers, which at present are still melting, will start growing again. At first this will be a slow, almost unnoticeable process, yard by yard, over a period of years. As more and more snow falls our grandchildren's domestic fuel bills will start to climb. Meanwhile, the glaciers will be growing slowly but surely. Ports today still free from ice will no longer be navigable in the winter months. Bitterly cold winds will invade our northern cities and in two or three thousand years' time a coat of ice nearly two miles thick will have buried Europe and North America.

Readings in every ocean do, in fact, indicate that the world is warming up, even though occasional winters may be colder than those of preceding years. Meteorologists have found that the temperature along the whole Pacific Coast has risen during the past six decades. Warm water flowing northward from the Atlantic has driven the cod away from Cape Cod to the colder regions off Newfoundland. Spitzbergen Harbor is now free from ice for twice as long as it was at the end of the last century.

"Even the Baltic will not freeze up as much in the next decade as it has done up to now," predicted the director of the Leningrad Oceanographic Institute at a scientific conference at Kiel in March, 1959.

Signs of a rising temperature on the mainland are equally evident. Dr. H. E. Landsberg of the American Meteorological Office reported, for example, that the vegetation boundary in Finnish Lapland had advanced three miles further north since 1930. American and Russian reports of polar expeditions agree in their finding that during the past fifty years the average annual temperature at the South Pole has risen by 7.5° Fahrenheit and at the North Pole by 15.3° Fahrenheit.

It seems obvious that the warming trend will lead to the breakup of the Arctic ice. Today, the frozen surface of the Arctic Ocean in summer is only about one-half of what it was at the turn of the century. Sea ice melting in the water naturally has no effect on the level of the sea. Of the 24 billion cubic yards of ice covering our earth, however, a large part consists of the mighty glaciers on the mainland. It is the melted water from these glaciers and from the vast Greenland icecap that in the last hundred years has raised the level of the sea by one foot, a situation which worries men like Ewing and Brooks.

All kinds of reasons are given by climatologists to explain why the earth is warming up. Some blame it on certain natural phenomena, such as an increased solar radiation. Others are convinced that man himself is responsible for the warming trend which some term a menace. "He has upset the age-old balance of nature," they say. "With the modern industrial age he has begun to pollute the air with industrial wastes, thus intensifying the so-called greenhouse effect tremendously."

The normal, very slight amount of carbon dioxide in the atmosphere (0.3 percent) is responsible to a considerable extent for the temperature of the earth's surface. This gas acts like the glass roof of a greenhouse. While it readily permits the passage of warming radiation in the form of wavelength emitted by the sun, it prevents the escape of this heat back into space. The more industrial carbon dioxide man injects into the atmosphere, the warmer it should get on the earth. According to Dr. Bert Bolin of Stockholm University, man is increasing the air's carbon dioxide content in a much greater measure than is actually permissible. Here are some figures: Since 1860 the chimneys of large industrial plants and since the turn of the century the exhausts of innumerable cars have emitted about 260 billion tons of carbon dioxide into the air. In 1960 alone 1,000 billion cubic feet of combustible gases were produced daily by the 70 million vehicles in America, while the annual amount of dust and soot falling upon New York from the city's exhausts amounts to about 260,000 tons.

Whether air pollution is actually to blame for the warming trend has yet to be proved. But there is little doubt that a continuous rise in temperature would have catastrophic results. C. E. P. Brooks, a British climatologist, estimated in 1961 that an additional world-wide rise of only two degrees would melt enough ice to send the sea flooding into much of New York, London and other great cities, as well as countless seaside towns.

Paradoxically it is this very flood which in Ewing's and Donn's opinion will evoke a new ice age. In their view the ice ages of the last million years have occurred when the Arctic Ocean was free of ice (just as it one day will be again if the present warming trend continues). To understand this theory better it should be pointed out that once, about one million years ago, there were no zones on earth where extreme heat or cold was prevalent. Palms and giant pewter grass used to grow in Greenland and the Antarctic, as numerous discoveries have shown, for the North Pole then was not where it is today, but in the middle of the Pacific. There, in the open sea, no masses of land existed on which snow and ice could have accumulated. In addition, the ocean currents saw to it that the cold did not concentrate in one spot, but was distributed over the whole globe. Then, as a result of tremendous geophysical processes in the earth's crust, the North and South Poles shifted. The North Pole shifted into an area enclosed by continents, while the South Pole moved onto a continent, which is now the Antarctic. In both cases the polar cold was prevented from being circulated any longer by ocean currents. Two climatically opposed zones arose. The Arctic Ocean froze up and thus, 600,000 years ago, began the first of four ice ages. According to Donn and Ewing, a fifth is now impending. The main cause of this devastating cycle is the Atlantic and the Arctic oceans, say the two scientists. The Arctic Ocean is almost completely surrounded by land. Its most important connection with another ocean, apart from the Bering Strait, which is narrow, is the 1,100-mile-wide passage between Greenland and Norway. At this point, which is not particularly deep because of an underwater ridge, the warm Atlantic waters mix with those of the Arctic Ocean, and gradually melt the latter's icecap. Its water will finally have a chance to evaporate, falling down as snow again on the glaciers of the mainland.

Glaciers are like sluggish lumps of dough. Every snowfall increases their weight and as the pressure on their base grows they start moving in the direction offering the least resistance. There are glaciers that slip a few inches per week, others that move up to thirty yards a day. The more snow that falls on the glaciers, the further south they will penetrate, eventually icing the continents with a thick frozen surface. The constant evaporation would lower the ocean levels foot by foot over a period of centuries. (It is known that at the height of the last ice age the sea level was three to four hundred feet lower than at its beginning.)

Once the sea level starts to fall, Ewing says, an ice age is on the point of receding. As so much water from the sea evaporates, the shelf between Greenland and Norway, which in places is only three hundred feet deep, will increasingly come to light. The exchange of water between the Atlantic and the Arctic oceans will be reduced until it ceases altogether. Then the Arctic Ocean will begin to freeze up again, since it is no longer receiving warm water. Evaporation will stop and the snowstorms subside. The weight of the glaciers will stop increasing, and their movement come to a halt. They will start melting under the warmth of the sun, and the water will flow back to the sea, whence it originated. The sea level will begin to rise and the exchange of warm water from the Atlantic with the Arctic water over the Greenland ridge will be resumed. The Arctic Ocean will warm up once more, causing its frozen surface to break up. And yet another flood will be on the way.

Ewing's theory had hardly become publicized before engineers were suggesting all kinds of countermeasures. With the assistance of "atomic suns" and carefully controlled atomic explosions, it was thought, enough ice could always be melted on the mainland to prevent the glaciers slipping southward. Another possibility suggested was space stations equipped with large mirrors to concentrate the sun's rays on the tips of the glaciers, to ensure a controlled thaw.

The most interesting suggestion, however, was made by Gail Hathaway, a civil engineer, who would like to tackle the evil at its root and avert future ice ages once and for all by preventing the flow of warm Atlantic water into the Arctic altogether. "The simplest thing," according to Hathaway, would be to build a gigantic dam stretching along the underwater ridge from Norway to Greenland. Its top would have to be about two hundred feet above the water surface. Apart from the enormous cost, construction of such a dam would be entirely feasible. It could be built of either concrete or ice. As we have already noted, exceptionally solid ice "alloys" have recently been developed. With the help of countless refrigeration coils it would be possible to freeze a whole "block" of sea water. Power stations using tidal motion and wind force could be built into the dam's ice wall to provide the power for the refrigeration equipment.

No theory is of any use without proof, so Ewing and Donn have for years been collecting evidence to support their views of the ice-age cycle. It is based mainly on the examination of ocean sediments, those fantastic witnesses of the earth's past millennia. These sediments are composed of the empty shells of single-cell creatures, crabs, snails, fossils of sponges, remnants of water lilies and sea urchins, mineral particles originating on the mainland and washed into the sea, micrometeorites from outer space, and finally even the harder skeleton parts of dolphins, whales and the almost insoluble teeth of sharks. For millions and millions of years layer has formed upon layer, like the pages of a vast history book of our planet. Although this book has grown at the rate of less than half an inch per millennium in some cases, it now displays a thickness of anywhere from one to twelve thousand feet, as indicated by depth soundings.

Using special equipment, oceanographers have long been able to raise sediment specimens from the ocean floor. The first cores punched out of the sea bottom were six to ten feet long. Since 1945 large numbers of thirty-five-foot cores have been brought to the surface, making it possible to examine deposits which date back to the late tertiary geological formation. In the light of such specimens the biological, geological and climatological history of the last thirty million years can be inferred accurately for the section of the ocean in question. With the so-called C_{14} test, by which the radioactivity of a given carbon isotope is measured, it is also possible to determine the age of individual samples with a fair amount of accuracy. In one instance cores from the bottom of the Mediterranean raised off the coast of Algeria showed that volcanoes had erupted there many thousands of years ago, a fact unknown until then.

In April, 1959, American oceanographers discovered an extensive layer of ash in the sediment in the Pacific Ocean off South America. In places it is as much as twelve inches thick and it covers an area of 308,875 square miles. Dr. Ewing believes that it arose from a series of terrific volcanic eruptions, which took place 68,000 years ago in the Andes. (This, incidentally, encouraged a theory that the ice ages might be attributed to dust or certain changes in the earth's atmosphere resulting from long periods of volcanic eruptions.) Geologists have also suggested obtaining several cores from the floor of the Mediterranean in order to find out when the Sahara came into being. Somewhere in the sediments at a certain depth there ought to be a strongly marked layer of sand, deposited on the ocean bed when winds coming from Africa first began to carry off the earth's crust from what is today known as the Sahara.

It was by turning back the pages of the earth's history book that Ewing and Donn learned important data which helped them to propound their theory of a coming ice age. On a voyage through the South Atlantic they discovered, for example, that in all cores obtained from the sea floor the top pink layer changed to gray after the first twelve inches. Examination under the microscope confirmed that the twelve-inch-thick pink sediment was composed of the shells of tiny warm-water creatures, as had already been suspected. The gray layer, on the other hand, contained the remains of organisms that preferred colder waters. That could only mean that the Caribbean, the Gulf of Mexico and the equatorial Atlantic where the cores were taken were once much colder than they are today. Then, about eleven thousand years ago, a climatic change took place. After its temperature had been dropping for millennia the Atlantic started warming up again. It was this observation that first supported Ewing's and Donn's theory. Eleven thousand years ago, they concluded, the exchange of water between the Atlantic and the then ice-free Arctic Ocean must have ceased. While the Arctic Ocean froze up, the last ice age ended and the Atlantic grew warmer.

Shortly after this discovery sediment samples from the floor of the Arctic Ocean showed that it must indeed at one stage have been free from ice. Once, for thousands of years, its waters had harbored vast amounts of marine life. Then, suddenly, as indicated by sediment samples, this life had disappeared. When the samples were dated the result was not surprising: life in the Arctic Ocean had ceased about eleven thousand years ago, or at the very time when, according to this theory, the ice age ended, the Atlantic began to warm up, and the Arctic Ocean began to freeze over.

The two American scientists received support for their theory from other sides as well: anthropologists and archaeologists found flint and other traces of human settlement on the shores of the Arctic Ocean. Experts dated them as being ten thousand years old and more. In what other way can settlement on the Arctic coast be explained, except by assuming that the Arctic Ocean was an open water during the last ice age?

In such mysterious ways does one branch of science overlap another. Innumerable tiny observations are often brought together to give significant results. What oceanographers have discovered in their sediment cores is of interest not only to meteorologists, but equally to archaeologists, biologists and geophysicists. Therefore, the deeper we can penetrate into the sea floor, the more accurate should be the picture of our planet's past, which in turn should help scientists to draw conclusions about its future.

This is one of the reasons why Russian and American oceanographers intend to devote their efforts to a more intensive study of the sediments of the sea floor, using some of the most modern equipment developed in recent years. A new sediment corer, for instance, will help them to obtain samples of undisturbed strata down to a depth of 160 feet and more. By 1970, it should be possible to punch sediment cores 330 feet in depth out of the ocean floor and hoist them to the surface.

Soviet scientists declare that "in the next twenty or thirty years the sedimentary deposits on the ocean floor will be studied in great detail." Professor Lev Senkyevitch explained in 1961 that on the basis of the samples obtained it will one day be possible to examine the process of evolution from its very beginnings. In other words, it should become possible for paleontologists to form a complete picture of how the life of the various species has developed from an original form into the creatures of the present. Naturally, for this purpose sediment cores far longer than 330 feet will have to be taken from the sea floor. This is one of the main objectives of "Project Mohole," an American scientific undertaking hopeful of flipping back the pages of the earth's history book to its very beginning.

19   The Mohole Project

In May, 1959, American research ships from various ports assembled 200 miles north of Puerto Rico to "mark off" a rectangle 250 miles long and 150 miles wide. Not long afterward, muffled explosions began to sound over the water, as the ships, traveling along predetermined courses, lowered depth charges into the sea at regular intervals. The echoes picked up from these seismic soundings enabled the scientists aboard the ships to find a suitable location for the Mohole Project: the drilling of a hole into the sea floor deep enough to pierce the earth's crust and reach the mantle of the planet, six miles below the water's surface. The discoveries thus made may one day be as important as those gained with the artificial earth and sun satellites of the U.S. space research program.

This gigantic drilling project planned by American scientists will mark man's greatest advance into the deep in search of his past. It should bring to light completely unknown layers of the deep-sea floor, for, just as very little was known about the mysteries of space only a few years ago, our present knowledge of the deepest layers of the ocean floor and about the interior of our planet is very scant. What knowledge we have is based on hypotheses or, at best, indirect observations, for no one has yet succeeded in raising samples of rock from these depths. "Project Mohole" will therefore prove or refute present-day theories on the formation of the earth's mantle and the lower layers of the earth's crust, which includes the ocean floor.

American research scientists hope that they will be able to tell from sediments found at these depths whether life really did begin two to three billion years ago, as is now supposed,

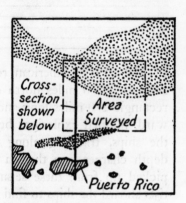

Schematic drawing shows area off Puerto Rico which had been surveyed as a possible site for the Mohole drilling. Drawing below is a cross-section through same area. It clearly indicates that a hole to the mantle of the earth (dotted area) would require less drilling if done from a barge out at sea than from the surface of an island.

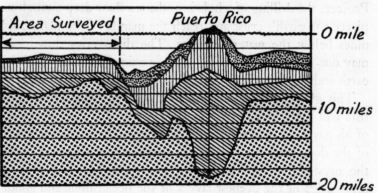

and how it has developed since. Drilling for oil on the mainland has allowed paleontologists to penetrate the sediments of former sea floors, and thus to establish an almost perfect picture of the history of evolution since the Cambrian formation, though this was "only" 500 million years ago. The oldest fossils discovered to date come from this period. But what forms of life existed before then? The Mohole Project may well be able to provide the information to fill this gap of 2.5 billion years.

Earth samples from the drilling will also provide meteorologists with a past record of the climate of our planet, and help to resolve such questions as polar wandering and continental drift, showing whether or not continents once moved across the basins of the oceans. Studying the orientation of metallic filaments in the sediment samples of various layers is one method that will help to determine the past locations of the magnetic poles. Deep down, on the earth's original crust, oceanographers will perhaps also find traces of how the oceans were formed, a process still understood only very incompletely. One theory is that the water was pressed out from the center of the earth through volcanic activity, at the time that the atmosphere first appeared, when the first rains fell on the planet and washed the earliest masses of earth and sand from the continents into the original sea. It is believed that the earth then began to take on its present shape.

If the hopes of the American drilling team are fulfilled, they should come upon meteorite dust somewhere at the bottom of the Mohole. This dust, which fell on the earth's original crust some three billion years ago, when the planet was still a heavenly body without air or water, is believed to be similar or identical to the dust assumed to be on the moon's surface. Perhaps the massive drilling operation will also confirm their assumption that the ocean floor is encrusted, scarred and crater-covered like the surface of the moon. In view of these extremely significant possibilities, it is understandable that many scientists call the Mohole "one of the most exciting adventures in the exploration of our planet."

The project was born in peculiar circumstances. In March, 1957, several prominent American scientists met at the California home of oceanographer Walter Munk for cocktails.

They all belonged to the American Miscellaneous Society (AMSOC), a group founded in protest against the bureaucratic red tape prevalent in many other scientific organizations. AMSOC has no statutes, no secretarial staff nor any formal membership list. In the early years of the society (founded in 1952) its meetings took the form of champagne or cocktail parties, and as spirits rose, the guests would outdo each other in the creation of utopian visions and projects. One of the projects was to tow icebergs from the Antarctic to the coast of California, where their fresh water could be used to irrigate the citrus plantations.

The idea, however, that bewitched AMSOC members most of all was the drilling of a hole deep into the planet. This idea was no new thing in itself. Imaginative writers like Jules Verne and Arthur Conan Doyle had written novels on related subjects. None other than Charles Darwin and later Maurice Ewing and Dr. Frank Eastbrook had tried to point out the advantages of sinking a shaft to the earth's interior. While these scholars, champagne glasses in hand, were discussing this project, they could hardly fail to take into account the success of modern drilling techniques. Suddenly the idea of sinking a hole in the earth to the depth of the Mohorovicic discontinuity, a rock layer between the earth's mantle and its crust, no longer seemed absurd at all. "Project Mohole" had been born.

It was quickly agreed that, with available techniques, "the simplest way" to pierce the earth's crust and reach the Moho was to conduct the drilling operations on the open sea. The reason was that the crust has no uniform thickness: on the continents it measures between twenty and thirty miles, out at sea and at a depth of about ten thousand feet, it is relatively thin, measuring in places only three to five miles.

When the Mohole Project was first conceived, drilling operations at sea were already at a fairly advanced stage of development. Hundreds of platforms, known as Texas towers, were being used off the Texas and Venezuelan coasts to drill down to the oil deposits of the continental shelf. But all these operations took place in shallow waters of not more than four hundred feet in depth, while the Mohole would have to be started in water more than two miles deep. This meant that instead of a tower firmly anchored in the earth, a floating platform would have to be used for drilling. AMSOC members decided, that *CUSS I*, a reconstructed Navy barge, already in use for drilling operations, seemed best suited for their purpose. Late in 1959 the Global Marine Exploration Company started modifying *CUSS I* for a number of trial drillings in deep waters, to precede the actual Mohole.

Meanwhile, a suitable location for these drillings had to be found, in favorable geological and climatic conditions. Any hurricane, any storm, or even prolonged rough seas and cold could endanger a drilling operation. Moreover, the area had to be free from strong surface and submarine currents to prevent damage to the drill pipe.

Two sites were finally approved for the project. The first was not far from the Puerto Rico trench, where the depth soundings mentioned earlier had shown that the sea floor there lay some fourteen thousand feet below the surface. Beneath that the bounds of the Moho area reached another 17,750 feet. The other area, finally chosen, lay in a relatively shallow part of the Pacific Ocean, between Guadalupe and the Clipperton Islands off the coast of Mexico. Here, the sea is about twelve thousand feet deep.

Favorable as it may sound, the selection of this place still called for the design and construction of a unique and highly unusual drill pipe. Weighing 110 tons and measuring more than two and one-half miles in length, it could not be supported by surrounding earth as it would be in an onshore drilling, but had to lead freely to the ocean bottom. It was planned that all holes would be uncased (in the preliminary drillings)—that is, the only connection between *CUSS 1* and the ocean bottom would be the drill pipe itself. This meant that once a bit had been withdrawn from the hole, it would be impossible to re-enter it. Therefore, all sampling and measuring operations would have to be conducted by the lowering of tools and instruments on a wire within the drill pipe itself.

As *CUSS 1* was to work in water too deep to permit the usual anchoring, the AMSOC staff conceived a highly original dynamic positioning system. By means of sonar, the ship was to sense its position relative to a ring of six buoys; these buoys were to be anchored to the bottom by taut wires and held two hundred feet beneath the surface of the water. Their distance from each other and from the floating drilling platform during the first experiments was about one thousand feet.

Using the sonar information, together with radar and visual sightings of surface buoys above the deep buoys, the pilot of *CUSS 1* was able to maneuver the ship so as to keep it in the center of the ring of buoys, and over the drilling hole. Simultaneously he was able to control the vessel's four outboard engines by means of a small handle resembling an aircraft "joy stick" on the control console. The direction and extent of the pilot's movements of the handle automatically regulated the direction and amount of thrust of all four engines so as to reposition the vessel.

Another device, an inclinometer, consisted of a light cable anchored to the sea floor to simulate the drill pipe. There it was attached to an instrument that determined the approximate bending of the pipe at the point where it entered the hole. This information was available to the pilot as an additional navigational aid.

The first test drilling, finally undertaken in March, 1961, was a complete success, and was hailed by some of the nation's leading scientists and engineers as signaling a new era in oceanography and geology. The test also proved that the technical approaches to the problem of deep-sea drilling, as conceived by the members of the project, will have far-reaching effects upon this country's mining and oil industry, making possible a better exploitation of our planet's hidden resources.

CUSS I, accompanied by several auxiliary vessels, left San Diego on March 23, arriving off Guadalupe Island three days later. There, after positioning the buoys, the individual strands of the drilling shaft were jointed together and then dropped through the center of the barge from a hundred-foot derrick. The diamond-studded drill bit touched bottom at 11,700 feet on March 28, and approximately nine hours later the first core was pulled up inside the drill pipe from a depth of 110 feet below the ocean bottom. While the scientists carefully inserted the core into long glass cylinders for later study, drilling continued until a depth of three hundred feet was reached. Again a core was to be pulled up. But this time the cable with the corer got stuck on the way up. When the cable finally broke there was not much else to do but pull up the whole drill string and start a new hole.

The tedious job of hoisting up the long pipe, dismantling it, removing the corer from the last pipe, and then assembling the drill string again and lowering it to the bottom lasted twenty hours. But this next time, work proceeded as planned and cores of soft, gray-green clay of Miocene age (approximately twenty million years old) were obtained down to a depth of 560 feet. At that depth the fast drilling speed abruptly decreased and when the core barrel was retrieved, it was found to contain bluish, hard, fine-grained basalt. This was the first time that a sample of the so-called second layer under the softer sediments of the ocean floor had ever been obtained. This layer, whose presence had been previously indicated to scientists only by the reflections of seismic soundings, was revealed to be basalt, a hard rock formed by the solidification of molten material within the earth. According to Dr. Harry S. Ladd, it formed about thirty million years ago, when molten lava, spewing up from the earth's interior, spread a thick carpet of basaltic rock on the ocean floor.

A second core of basalt ten feet long was then obtained. Drilling continued, and gradually the samples brought up with the corer changed from basalt to gray mud, mixed with pieces of basalt, volcanic ash and dolomite, a rock which no longer forms on the ocean floor. The mud contained some sea fossils and age-old mainland sediments. Gordon Lill, leader of the Mohole Project, later explained that the fossils might be from the Cretaceous period, which extended from seventy to a hundred million years ago, but only more drilling can pinpoint the age. This is one of the aims of the present Mohole activities.

The super-drilling, planned for some time in 1964 (if the necessary funds can be made available), will be immensely more complicated than the preliminary tests. The water may be as much as 18,000 feet deep (3.4 miles) and a new barge—though based on the experiences gained with *CUSS I*—will have to be constructed to hold the contemplated 35,000 feet of drilling pipe.

Since the actual Mohole will penetrate partly through rock rather than the soft bottom sediments alone the drilling shaft will have to be cased with a pipe (as in mainland oil drillings) so that a solution of mud and water can be pumped down to the drill bit to cool it and carry away the drilling debris. The casing, at the same time, will assure that a hole, once started, will not get "lost" again if the drill bit for some reason or other has to be raised. The Mohole will therefore be much costlier than the preliminary tests, and the drill will penetrate well below the second (basalt) layer. The temperature in the hole may rise to over 400° Fahrenheit shortly before the drill bit reaches the Moho layer. Some geologists expect the strata in the Moho to be so soft that they will actually flow back into the hole or be forced up in the casing like a mass of spaghetti dough.

When the drill bit finally scratches the earth's mantle after three to four years of work there will be a hole extending almost three miles into the interior of our planet—six miles, if you add the distance from sea bottom to the surface. Geologists and geophysicists expect the second phase of the Mohole Project to provide important information about the construction of the earth's interior and what goes on there.

The U.S. Navy, petroleum and mining companies and salvage concerns are showing considerable interest in the Mohole Project as well, since it will help improve certain methods in oil drilling and marine technology. Modern deep-sea winches now in use on board several ships, for instance, have a lifting capacity of about five tons. AMSOC members think they will be able to let down much greater loads of up to a hundred tons with the aid of their drilling pipe. Once these loads are on the sea floor it should be possible, again with the drill pipe, to move them into any desired position. In this way, for example, concrete foundations could be laid on the ocean floor, and buildings for deep-sea submarines or rocket bases erected. Such structures would also make it much easier to obtain minerals from the ocean floor.

Though such projects still lie very far in the future, the Russians seem to have recognized their significance, as well as the scientific values of a "Mohole" of their own. American scientists had hardly voiced the first intimations of their audacious project in 1957, when some of their Eastern colleagues rushed to announce that "the Soviet Academy of Sciences also intends to probe the earth's mantle. We possess the necessary technical knowledge. What we are looking for is a suitable place." Four years later, in August of 1961, Radio Moscow announced that not only one but several places had been found and that a number of drillings "surpassing the American Mohole in magnitude and significance had been started." The planned depth of the mightiest Soviet drilling was given as "ten to fifteen miles," and its location was a volcanic island in the Kuriles. Surprisingly, Soviet scientists expressed preference for a drilling site on land, which would mean having to build a fifteen-mile-deep hole in order to reach the Moho, but would eliminate the complex steering and stabilizing mechanism needed on a floating platform. One reason the Russians may be able to drill this deep is that they use turbine drills. The motor that turns the drill bit is located directly above it at the lower end of the drill pipe, sinking down into the well the deeper it is drilled. Mohole scientists, on the other hand, use the rotary method of the U.S. petroleum industry, in which the motor stays on the surface and the drill pipe is rotated from above in its total length. Naturally in this method a lot of energy is diverted merely to rotate the pipe, with the drill bit itself getting the benefit of only a portion of the total power.

In addition to the boring in the Kuriles four more holes will be drilled within the Soviet Union. At the time of this writing it is known that the first is to be driven into the earth's crust in Karelia in northwest European Russia. They hope to pierce through the granite layers of the earth, whose age is believed to exceed 3.5 billion years. The depth of the hole, if completed successfully, would be about nine miles.

The second of four planned "small" drillings will be undertaken near the northern shore of the Caspian Sea, also to a depth of nine miles. From these drillings, Soviet scientists expect to gain information on eventual petroleum formations in deep layers.

"By the year 2000," Professor Tscherbakov confidently announced late in 1961, "we shall have discovered methods of obtaining valuable oil from the sea and mainland at depths of seven to ten thousand and more feet." There can be little doubt that the Russians intend to reach the earth's crust ahead of the American Mohole team. With the generous financing already promised them by the Soviet government they will very likely succeed. This would be a bitter blow to our scientists, who literally broke the ground for these magnificent probes into the earth's interior, but are still struggling to finance their next test drillings.

Conclusion

As this book goes into print, it seems as though the efforts of the scientific community, of government agencies and members of Congress to strengthen the position of America's oceanography are bearing fruit. A number of new research and survey ships are being designed. The U.S. Navy has let construction contracts for two large military vessels and one for military survey activities. They are scheduled to become operational in 1964. The Coast and Geodetic Survey's fiscal plans for 1963 call for the construction of one 300-ton, one 1,200-ton, and two 750-ton coastal charting ships in addition to one 3,000-ton, one 1,200-ton and one 750-ton ocean survey ship. The larger ships will also be used for deep-sea oceanography. The Bureau of Commercial Fisheries also is building four new ships (however, three of these will be replacements).

At the same time, a great deal of public interest in oceanography has developed. Universities report a distinct rise in applications of students interested in marine sciences. Some institutions, where the space and funds were available, have been able to increase enrollment of qualified candidates by 50 to 100 percent during the past two years.

Most promising of all, however, is the fact that despite our efforts to meet the Russian challenge for a "race to inner space," this country has not lost sight of the higher goal of international cooperation. The United States, together with a

252

number of other nations, including the Soviet Union, has started an all-out attack on a water body that covers some 14 percent of the earth's surface, and about whose mysteries virtually nothing is known in 1962. In the so-called International Indian Ocean Expedition, a four-year exploration program, sixteen oceanographic ships are undertaking a thorough investigation of the Indian Ocean.

This vast sea was not chosen as the first point of attack purely by chance. Not only is it the least known of all water bodies, but on its shores lives one-quarter of the world's population. A large proportion of these people is poor and under-nourished, and in the history of mankind it has often been hunger that has sparked off a universal conflagration. There is evidence, however, that the ocean at their doorstep contains sufficient fish to make up the protein deficiency that exists in India, Ceylon, Indonesia, Malaya and points along the east coast of Africa, and that the waters surrounding Thailand, Cambodia and Vietnam may be the richest natural resources those countries have, and possibly the richest waters in the world.

In the coming years 125 scientists from eleven countries, including the U.S., the United Kingdom, Russia and Western Germany, will try to find the answers to these vital questions. They also want to know the reason why vast numbers of certain species of fish die so mysteriously in the Gulf of Arabia. They want to know more about the puzzling migrations undertaken so suddenly by many shoals of fish, which cause India's fishermen to return empty-handed so frequently. They would also like to discover what effects the monsoons have on the currents and upper regions of the water in the Indian Ocean, and what the ocean looks like at the bottom. A similar program, incidentally, is slowly getting under way for the Pacific Ocean.

Encouraged by the international cooperation evident so far

in the exploration of the Indian Ocean, the United States has
gone even one step further and suggested a program for inter-
governmental investigation of the world's seas to "increase the
contribution of oceanography to the general welfare of mankind."

The plan considered by the International Oceanographic
Commission (IOC) of the United Nations Educational, Scientific, and Cultural Organizations (UNESCO) would place
all oceanographic research, including data exchange and a proposed oceanographic forecasting network, under supervision by
the IOC. It seems vital that this or a similar plan be accepted
and followed through by the major powers of the world. Otherwise their struggle among each other for the control of the sea
will only become fiercer and fiercer with every year, until
finally a wet war will be waged before our eyes with the most
modern equipment of marine science and technology. Unless
there is cooperation from the start, the loser in this contest will
have no prospect of overcoming the beginning scarcity of mainland raw materials and will be unable to survive economically.
There is no doubt that the future of all life on our planet will
one day be decided in the very ocean where it once began.

Acknowledgments

Books

Allgemeine Meereskunde, by Günter Dietrich and Kurt Kalle, Gebrüder Bornträger, Berlin-Nikolassee, Germany, 1957.

Den Göttern gleich, by Dieter Stolze, Kurt Desch Verlag, Munich, West Germany, 1959.

Der grosse Fluss im Meer, by Hans Leip, Paul List Verlag, Munich, West Germany, 1955.

Der unzähmbare Ozean, by Hans Wolfgang Behm, Safari Verlag, Berlin, Germany, 1956.

Die Deutschen Waffen und Geheimwaffen des 2. Weltkrieges, by Rudolf Lusar, J. F. Lehmanns Verlag, Munich, West Germany, 1959.

Frontiers of the Sea, by Robert C. Cowen, Doubleday and Co., Inc., New York, 1960.

Menschen und Meerestiefe, by Rudolf Lange, Langewiesche-Brandt K. G., Munich, West Germany, 1957.

Nahrung und Rohstoffe aus dem Meer, by W. Rudolph, Wissenschaftliche Verlagsgesellschaft, Stuttgart, West Germany, 1948.

Nautilus 90 North, by Commander William R. Anderson, USN, World Publishing Co., Cleveland, 1959.

Polaris, by James Baar and William Howard, Harcourt, Brace and Co., New York, 1961.

Reportage aus dem 21. Jahrhundert, by M. Wassiljew and
    S. Guschtschov, Henry Nannen Verlag, Hamburg, West
    Germany, 1959.
Seven Miles Down, by Jacques Piccard and Robert S. Dietz,
    G. P. Putnam's Sons, New York, 1961.
The Deep Range, by Arthur C. Clarke, Harcourt, Brace and
    Co., New York, 1957.
The Ocean River, by Henry Chapin and F. G. Walton Smith,
    Charles Scribner's Sons, New York, 1953.
The Sea and Its Mysteries, by John S. Colmann, G. Bell and
    Sons, London, 1952.
The Sea Around Us, by Rachel Carson, Oxford University
    Press, New York, 1950.
The Soviet Navy, edited by Commander M. G. Saunders, RN,
    Frederick A. Praeger, New York, 1958.
The Story of the Oceans, by John S. Douglas, Dodd, Mead
    and Co., New York, 1952.
Wie werden wir leben?, by Walter Greiling, Econ-Verlag,
    Düsseldorf, West Germany, 1954.

Periodicals

All Hands (Navy publication)
Aviation Week, McGraw-Hill publication
Die Welt, Hamburg, West Germany
Die Zeit, Hamburg, West Germany
Fortune, Time-Life Inc.
Hobby, Ehapa Verlag, Stuttgart
Izvestia
Look
Life, Time-Life Inc.
Missiles and Rockets
National Geographic Magazine
Navy (Service magazine)

New York Times
Newsweek
Pravda
Product Engineering, McGraw-Hill publication
Red Fleet (Soviet Navy publication)
Rudder
Science News Letters
Soviet Union
Stern, Henry Nannen-Verlag, Hamburg, West Germany
Time, Time-Life Inc.
VDI-Nachrichten, Düsseldorf, West Germany

Other Sources

Possible Nonmilitary Scientific Developments and Their Potential Impact on Foreign Policy Problems of the United States, a study prepared at the request of the Committee on Foreign Relations, U.S. Senate, by Stanford Research Institute, No. 2, September, 1959.

Oceanography 1960 to 1970, a report by the Committee on Oceanography, National Academy of Sciences National Research Council.

Ocean Sciences and National Security, Report of the Committee on Science and Astronauts, U.S. House of Representatives, 86th Congress, July 1, 1960.

Advancement of Marine Sciences—Marine Sciences and Research Act of 1961, Report No. 246, 87th Congress.

Marine Science, Hearings before the Committee on Interstate and Foreign Commerce, U.S. Senate, 87th Congress, First Session on S. 901 and S. 1189, Bills to Advance the Marine Sciences, March 15, 16, 17 and May 2, 1961.

Drilling Thru the Earth's Crust, National Academy of Sciences National Research Council, 1959, and other releases by the AMSOC Committee on the Mohole Project, 1960–61.

Radioactive Waste Disposal into Atlantic and Gulf Coastal Waters, National Academy of Sciences National Research Council, 1959.

Radioactive Waste Disposal from Nuclear Powered Ships, National Academy of Sciences National Research Council, 1959.

Index

About the Author

Cord-Christian Troebst was born in 1933 in Bucharest, Rumania, where his father was a foreign correspondent for a German news service. He traveled with his parents to Manchuria via India and the Philippines, and in 1938, after the death of his father in China, returned with his mother to Rumania, where he spent the early years of World War II.

With the advance of the Russian armies, he and his mother left for Germany, an adventurous trip during which they were fired on by both the Russians and the Rumanians.

Mr. Troebst graduated from the Gymnasium Josephinum in Hildesheim, where he studied the natural sciences, in 1953. He subsequently joined the staff of the German popular science magazine, *Kristall*, published in Hamburg, and became assistant editor.

Two years later he spent the winter touring the Middle East on assignment for several West German newspapers, and on his return in 1956 met and married his wife, Ingrid. They emigrated to the United States in 1957, and plan to become citizens in 1962. Mr. Troebst worked for an American publisher until 1959 and then left to devote full time to free-lance writing. He has contributed to a number of West German and Swiss newspapers and magazines, and his first book on space developments, *Grasping for the Moon*, has gone into three printings in the German edition and was a selection of the German Book of the Month Club. It has been translated into eight languages.

Format by Stanley Wheatman
Set in Linotype Janson
Manufactured by American Book–Stratford Press
HARPER & ROW, PUBLISHERS, INCORPORATED